© 2006 by International Music Publications Ltd
First published by International Music Publications Ltd in 2006
International Music Publications Ltd is a Faber Music company
3 Queen Square, London WC1N 3AU

Photography Timm Cleasby www.fifty-50.co.uk
Designed by Timm Cleasby & Andy Nicholson
Arranged by Alex Davis
Engraved by Camden Music
Edited by Lucy Holliday & Olly Weeks

Printed in England by Caligraving Ltd
All rights reserved

ISBN 0-571-52556-3

Reproducing this music in any form is
illegal and forbidden by the
Copyright, Designs and Patents Act, 1988

To buy Faber Music publications or
to find out about the full range of titles available,
please contact your local music retailer or
Faber Music sales enquiries:

Faber Music Ltd, Burnt Mill, Elizabeth Way, Harlow,
CM20 2HX England
Tel: +44(0)1279 82 89 82
Fax: +44(0)1279 82 89 83
sales@fabermusic.com fabermusic.com

the view from the afternoon

Words and Music by Alex Turner

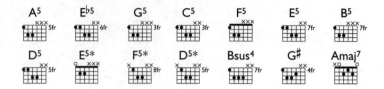

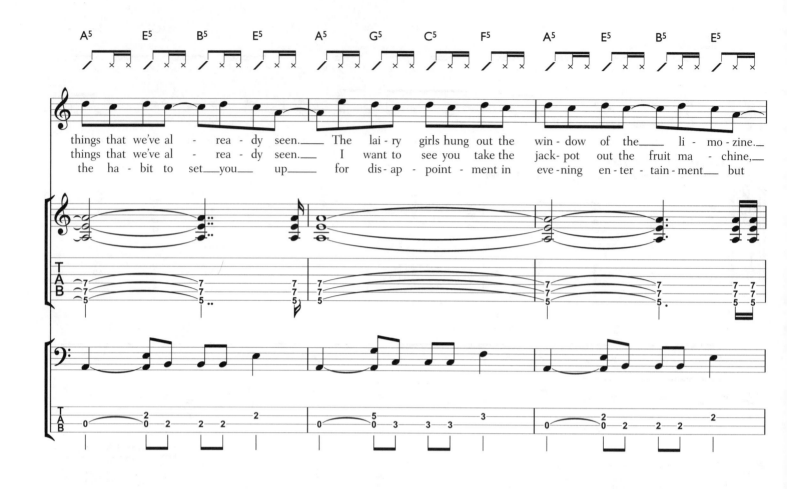

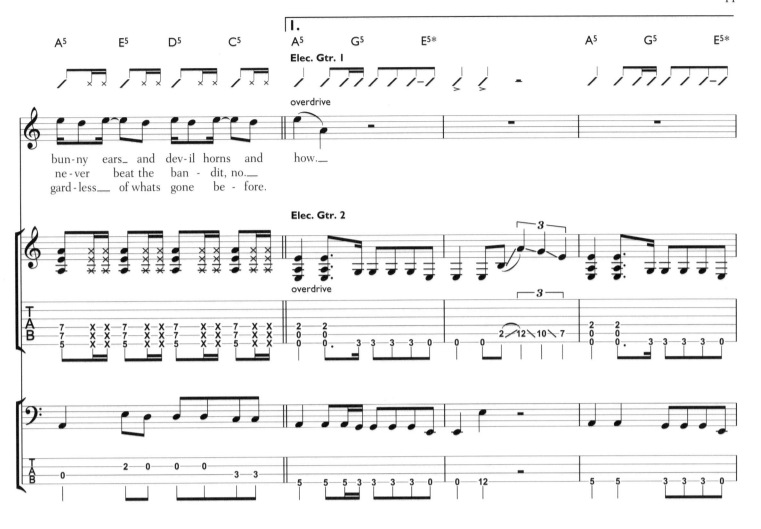

bun-ny ears_ and dev-il horns and how._
ne - ver beat the ban - dit, no._
gard-less_ of whats gone be - fore.

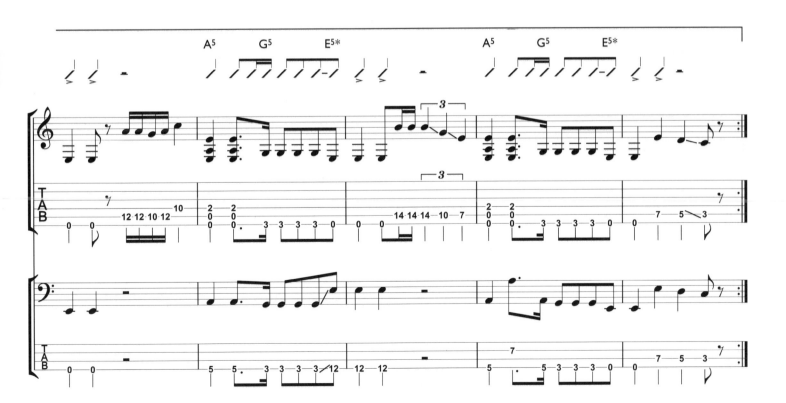

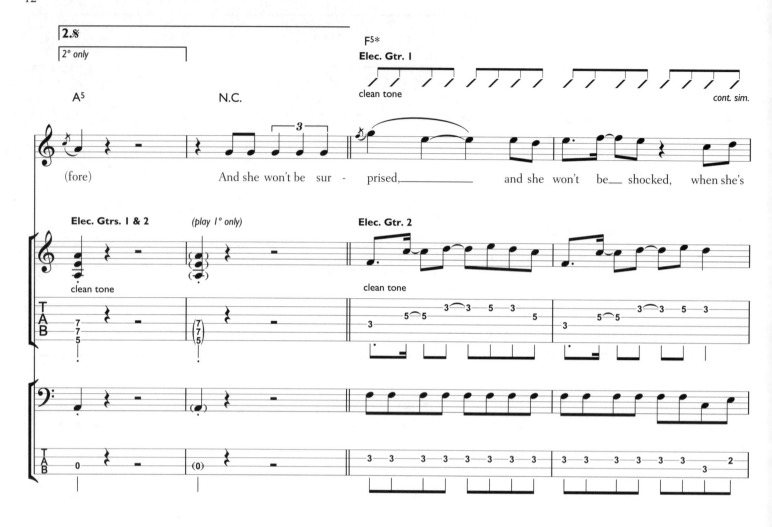

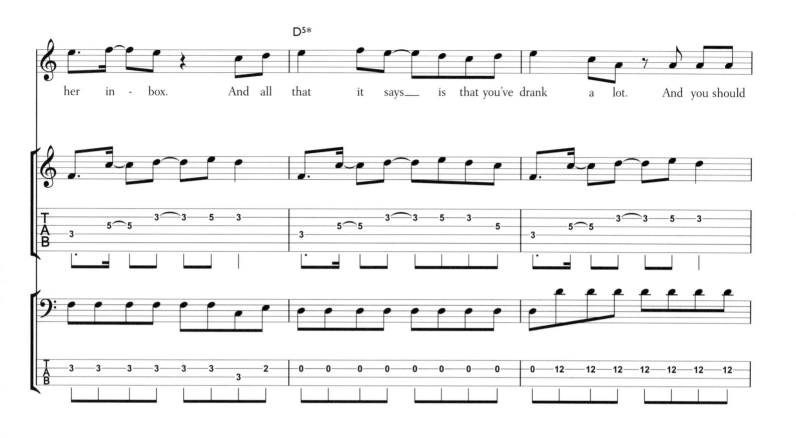

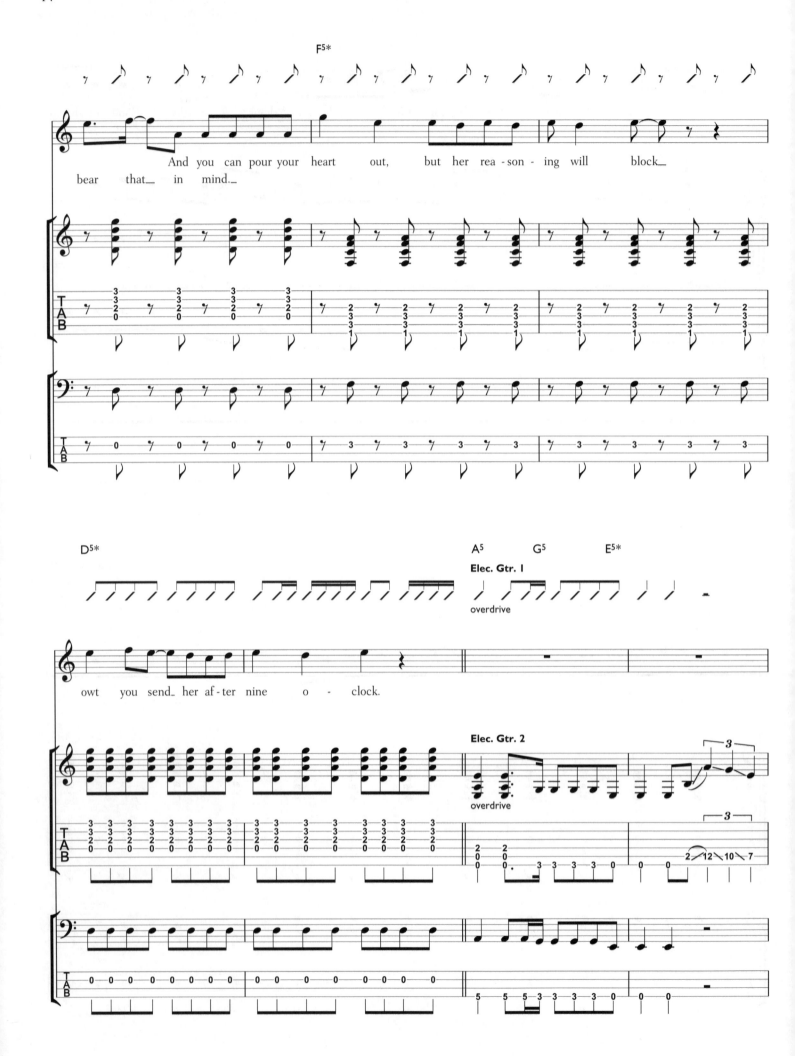

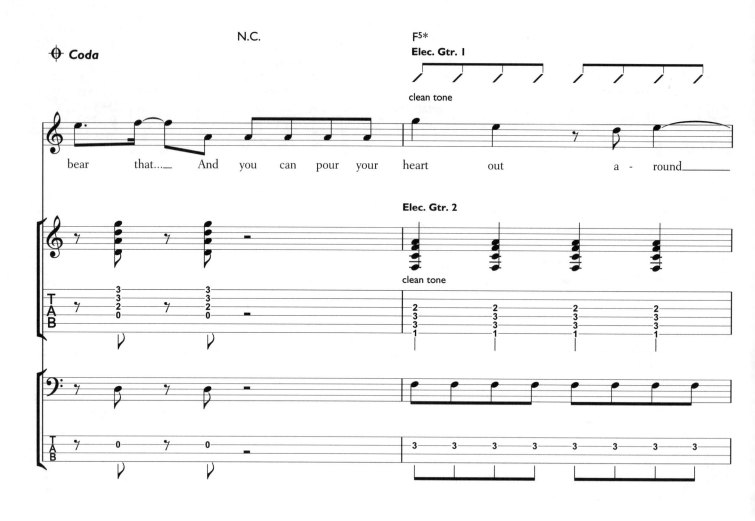

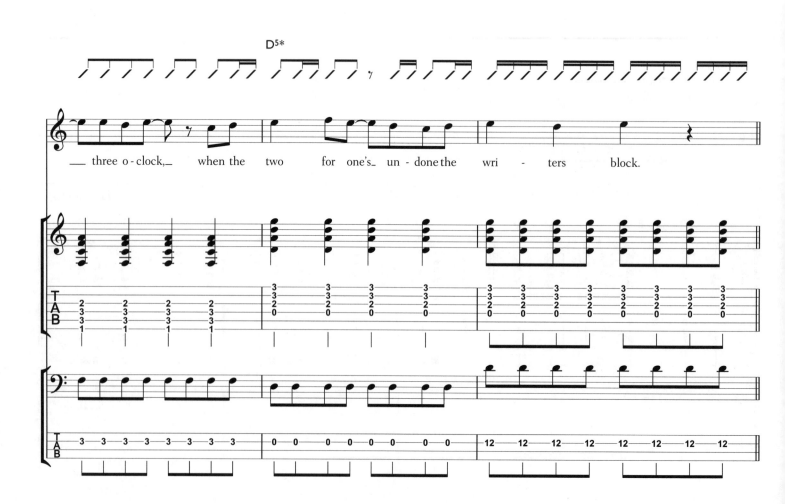

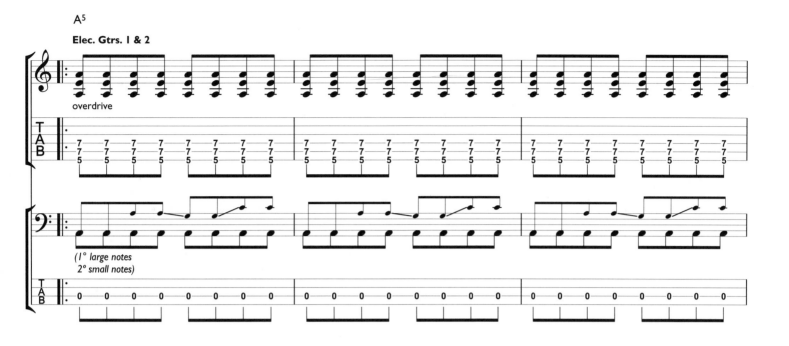

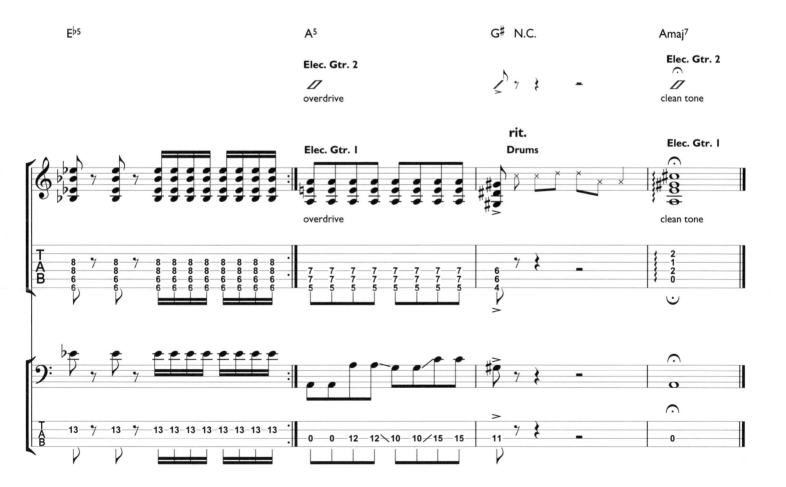

i bet you look good on the dancefloor

Words and Music by Alex Turner

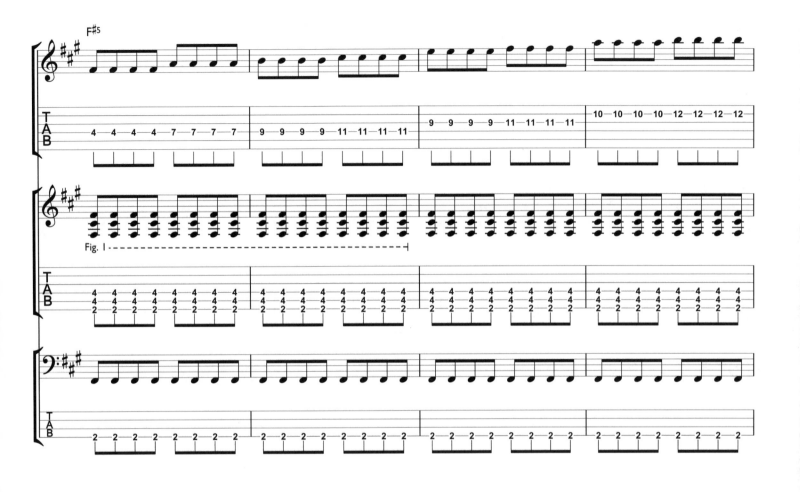

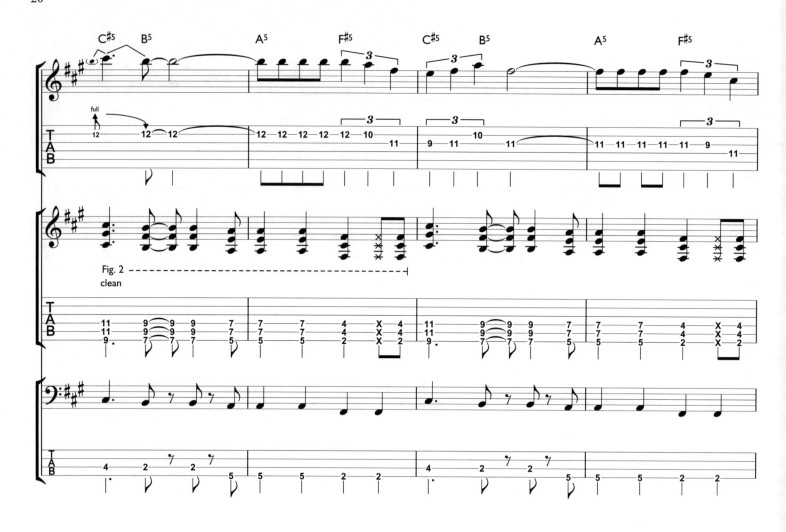

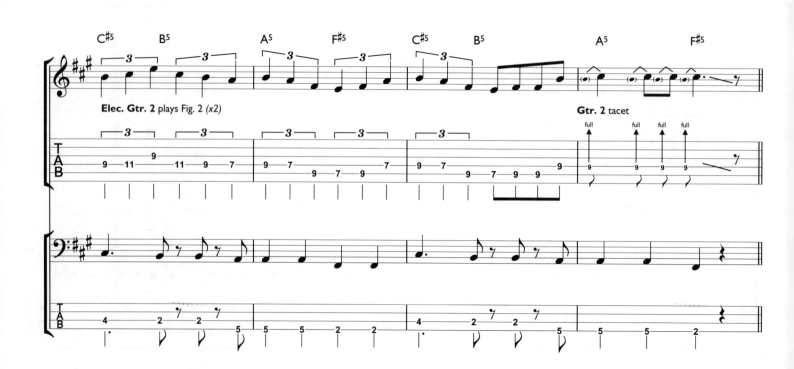

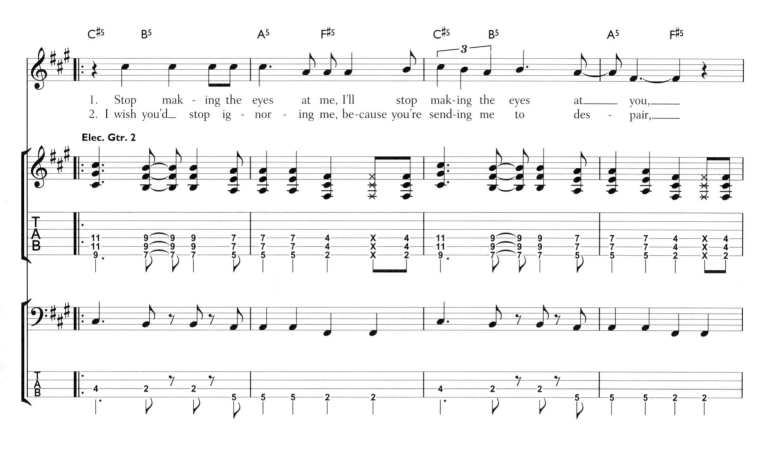

Elec. Gtr. 2

1. Stop mak-ing the eyes at me, I'll stop mak-ing the eyes at_____ you,_____
2. I wish you'd_ stop ig - nor - ing me, be-cause you're send-ing me to des - pair,_____

and what it is that sur - pri - ses me, is that I don't real - ly____ want you to. And your shoul-ders are
with - out a sound yeah you're call - ing me, and I don't think it's____ ve - ry fair, that your shoul-ders are

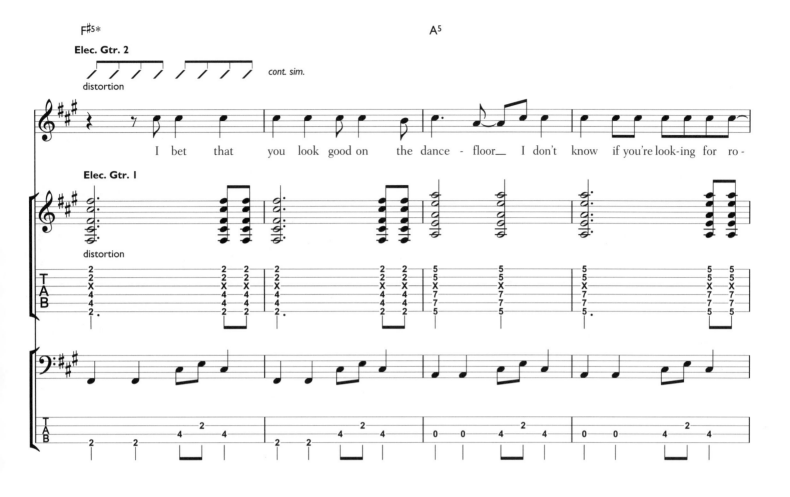

I bet that you look good on the dance - floor___ I don't know if you're look-ing for ro -

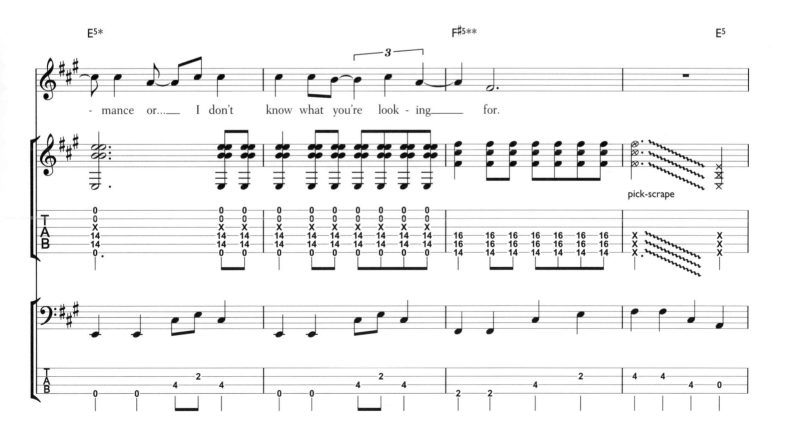

- mance or.....___ I don't know what you're look - ing___ for.

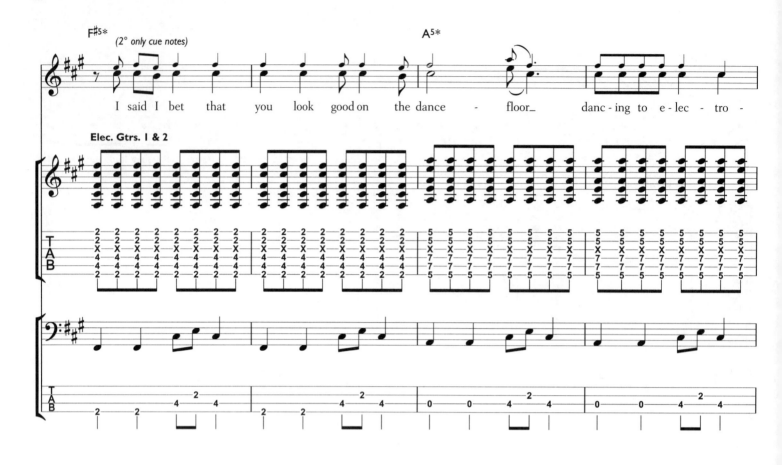

I said I bet that you look good on the dance - floor_ danc-ing to e-lec-tro-

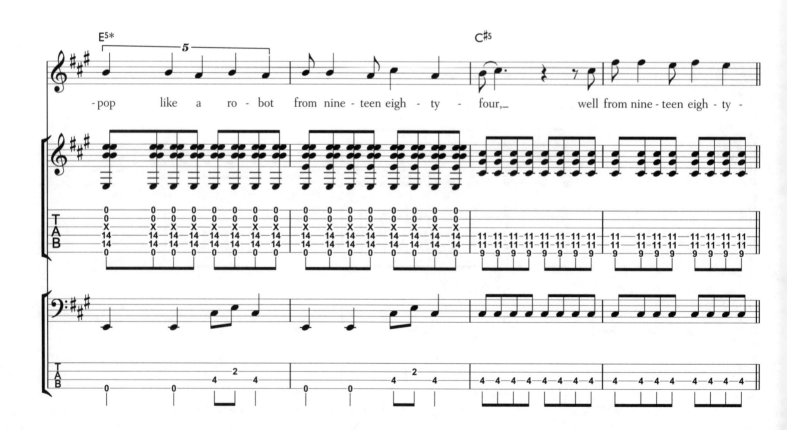

-pop like a ro-bot from nine-teen eigh-ty - four,_ well from nine-teen eigh-ty-

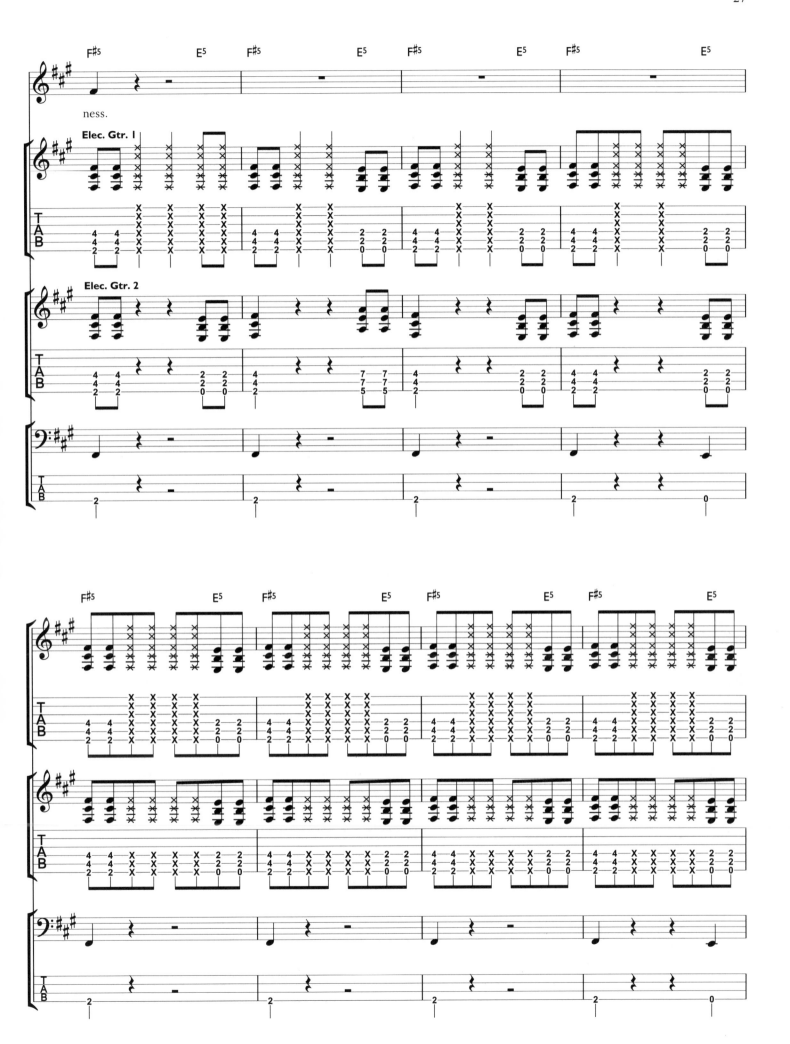

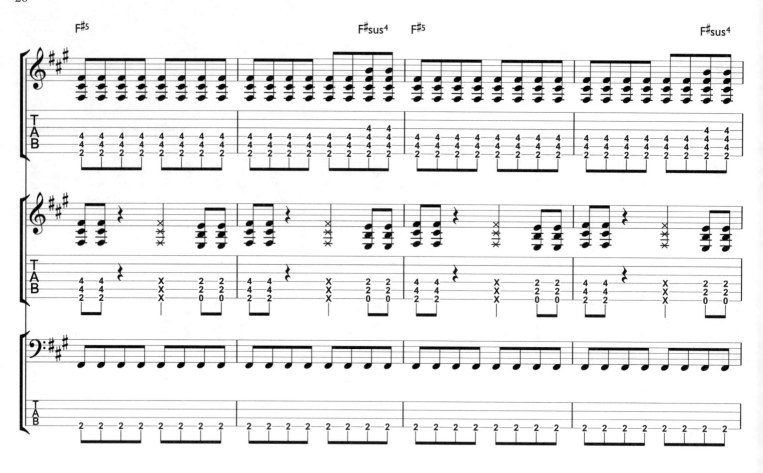

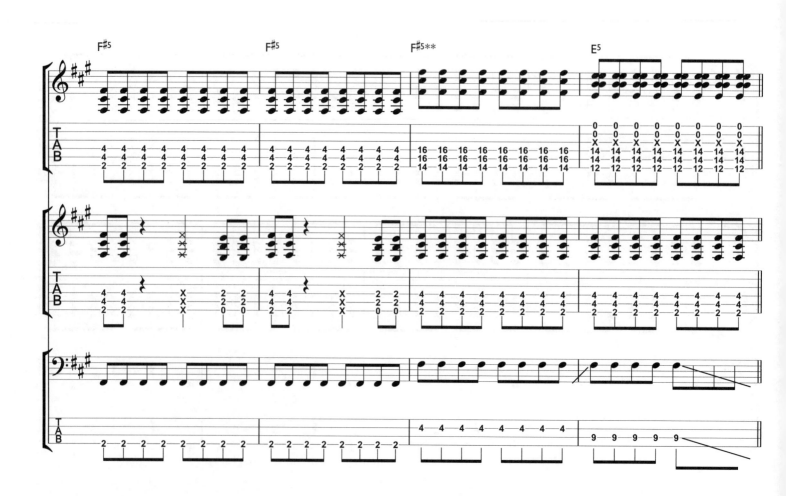

Uh well I bet that you look good on the dance - floor__ I don't know if you're look-ing for ro-

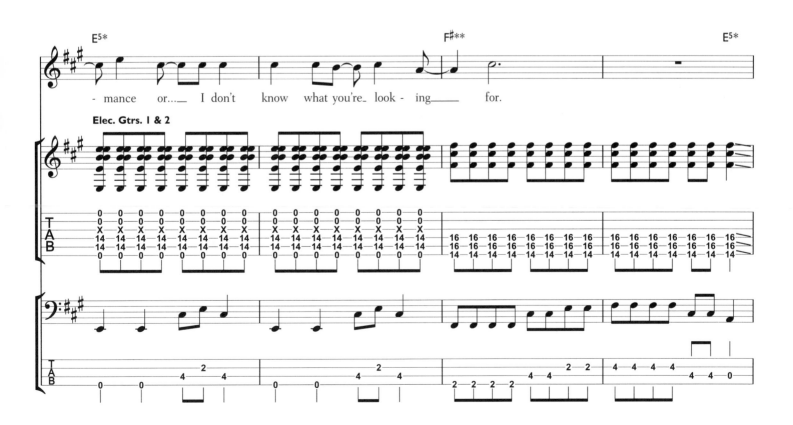

- mance or..._ I don't know what you're_ look - ing_____ for.

Elec. Gtrs. 1 & 2

fake tales of san francisco

Words and Music by Alex Turner

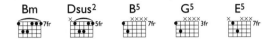

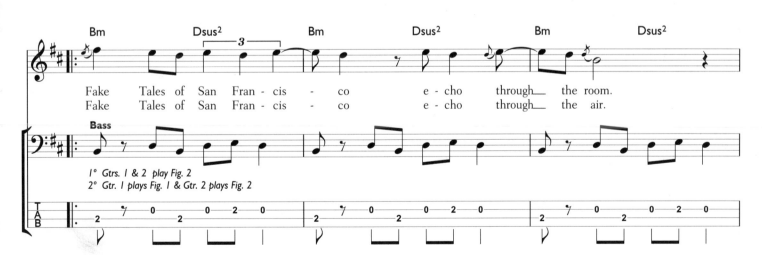

34

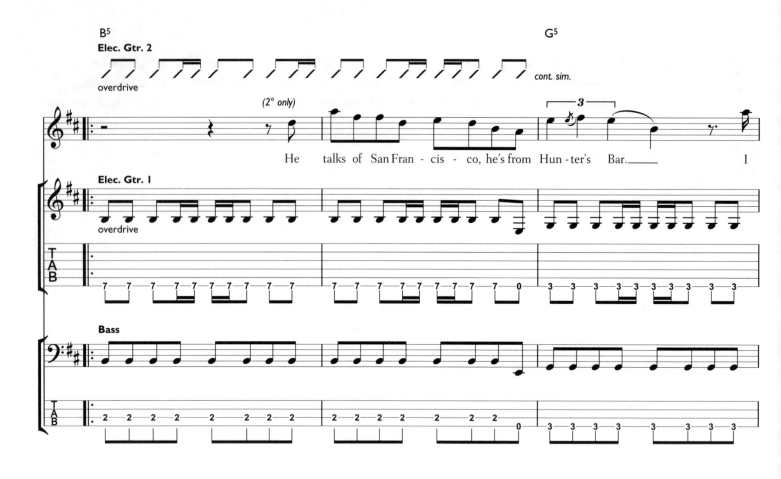

dancing shoes

Words and Music by Alex Turner

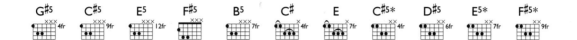

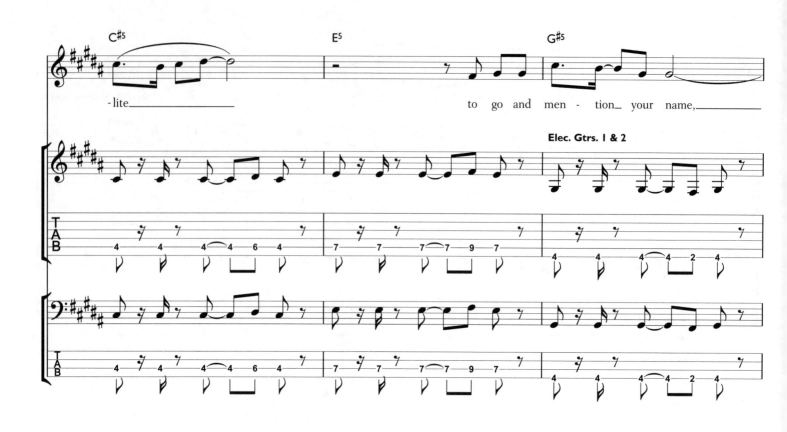

Get on your danc - ing_____ shoes,_____ you sex - y lit - tle__

48

Oh but it's oh___ so ab - surd_____ for you to say the first word, so you're wait - ing and wait - ing.

you probably couldn't see for the lights
but you were looking straight at me

Words and Music by Alex Turner

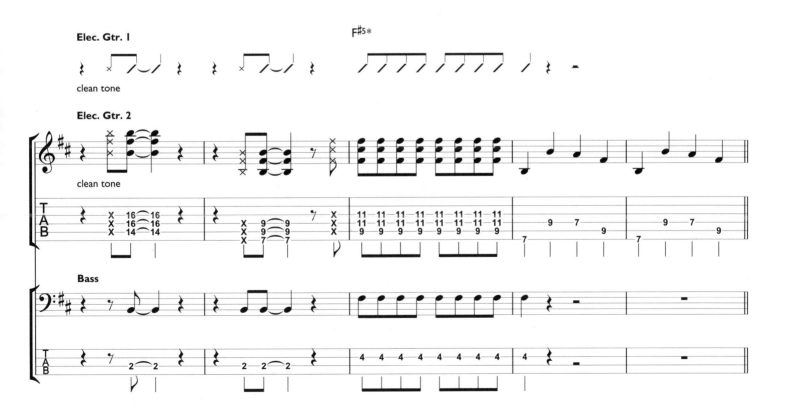

To Coda

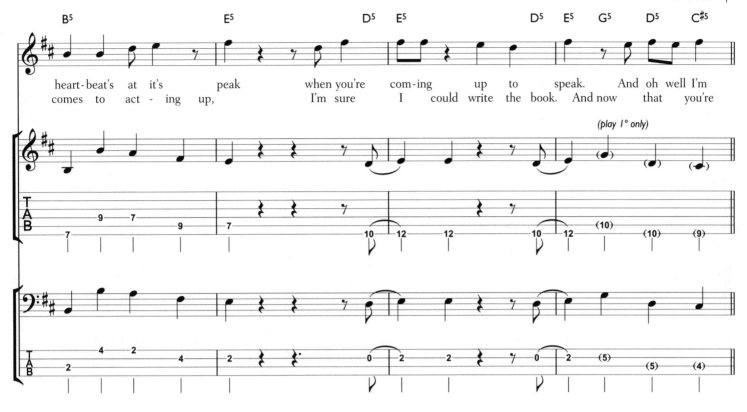

heart-beat's at it's peak when you're com-ing up to speak. And oh well I'm
comes to act - ing up, I'm sure I could write the book. And now that you're

(play 1° only)

Elec. Gtr. 1

clean tone

so tense, ne-ver ten - ser. Could all go a bit___ Frank Spen-cer?

Elec. Gtr. 2

overdrive

And I'm talk - ing gib - ber - ish,___ tip of the tongue but I can't de - li - ver it___

...pro - per - ly,___ oh it's all get - ting on top of me.___ And if it

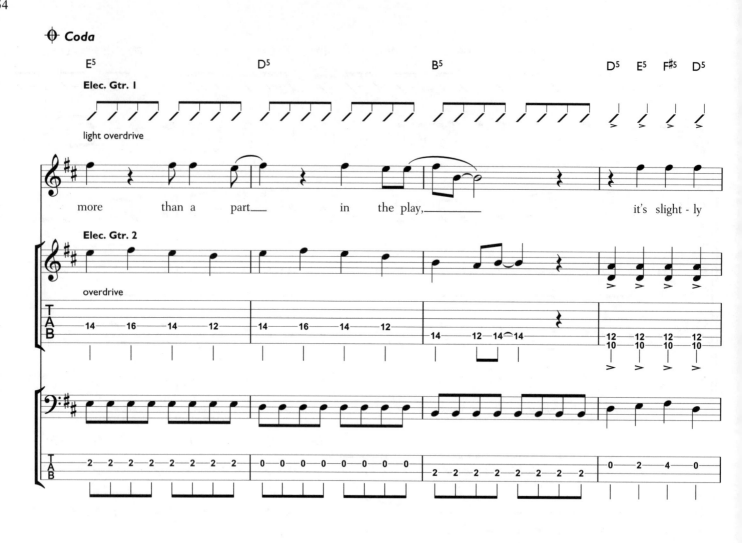

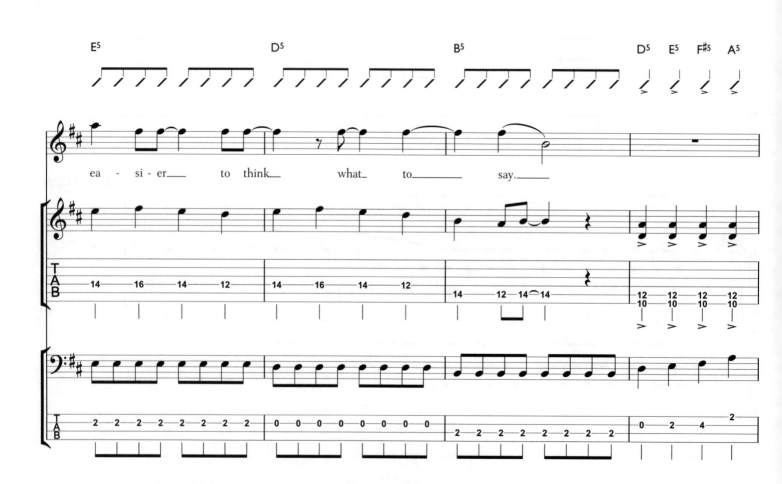

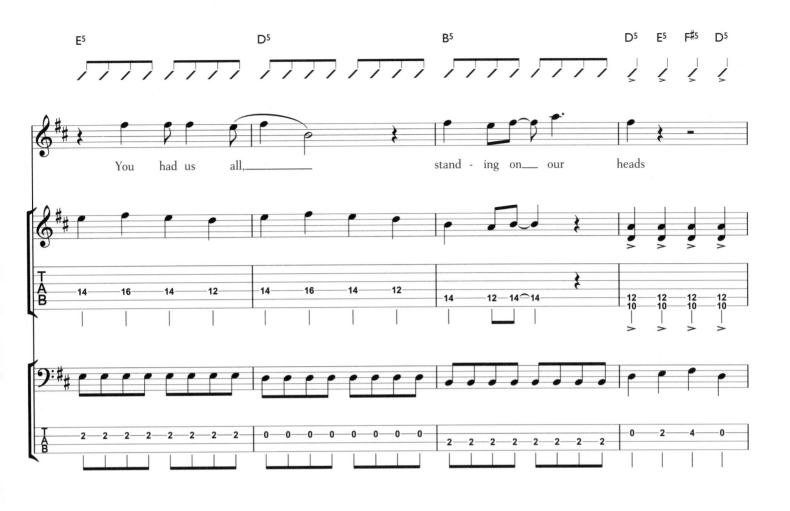

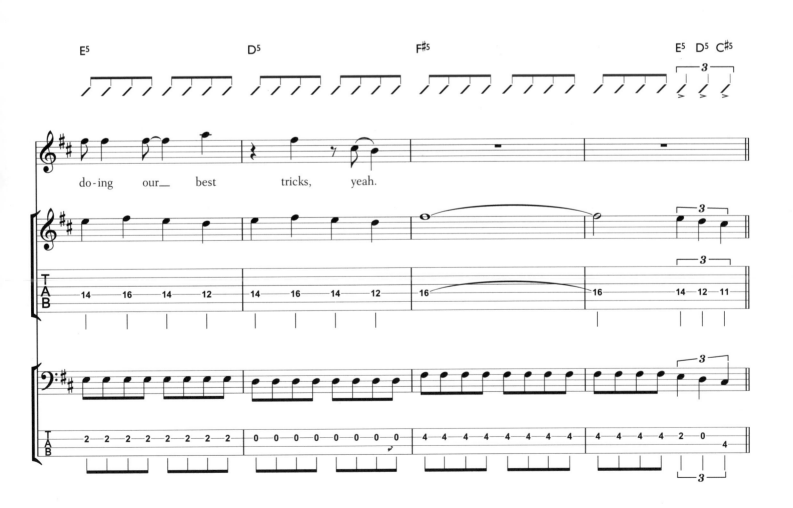

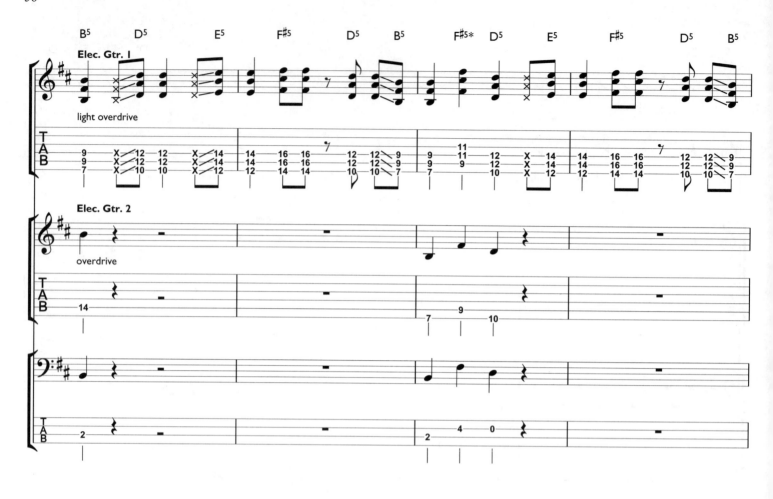

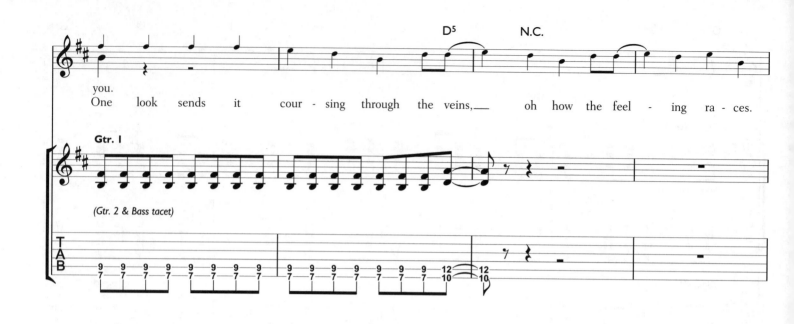

One look sends it cour-sing through the veins,___ oh how the feel - ing ra - ces.

Back up to their brains to form ex - pres - sions on their stu - pid fa - ces.

still take you home

Words and Music by Alex Turner and Jamie Cook

Well it's ev- er so fun- ny, 'cause I don't think you're spe -cial, I don't think you're cool.—
Well fan -cy see-ing you in— here, you're all— tar - ted up and you don't look the same.

Elec. Gtr. 1 *(1° only)*

light overdrive

Elec. Gtr. 2 *(2° only)*

light overdrive

(2° Bass tacet until *)

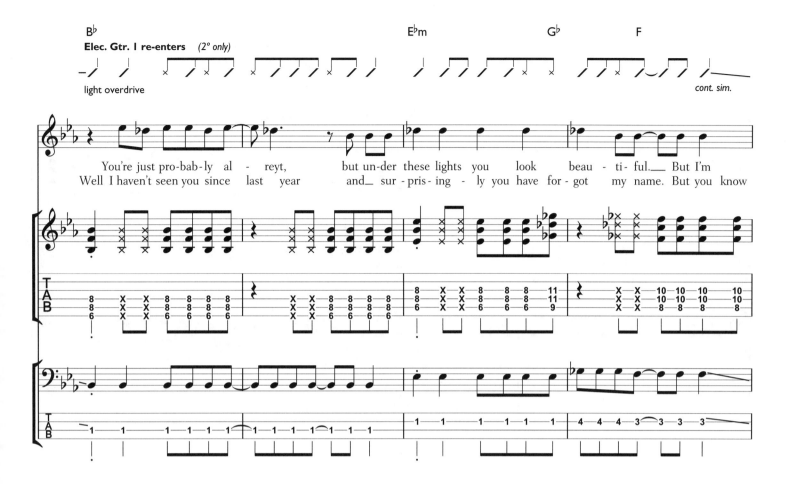

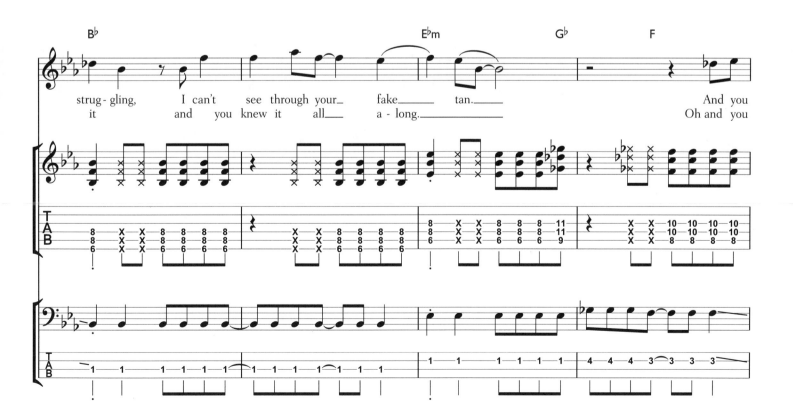

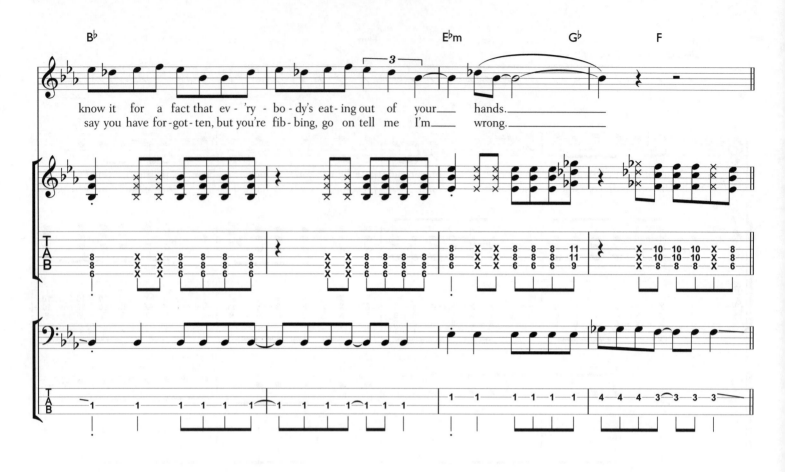

know it for a fact that ev - 'ry - bo - dy's eat - ing out of your___ hands.___
say you have for - got - ten, but you're fib - bing, go on tell me I'm___ wrong.___

But } what do you___ know?___ Oh,___ you know no - thing.
So }

light overdrive

Elec. Gtr. 1

light overdrive

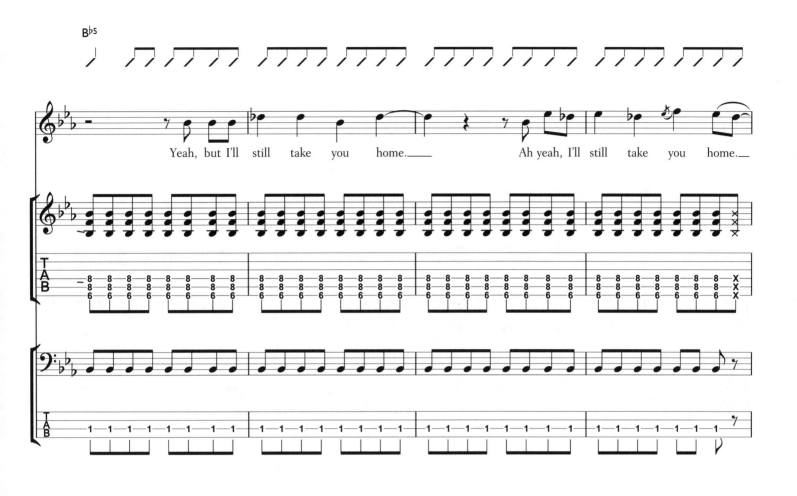

Yeah, but I'll still take you home.___ Ah yeah, I'll still take you home.___

___ So what do you__ know?_____ Said you don't know no-thing.

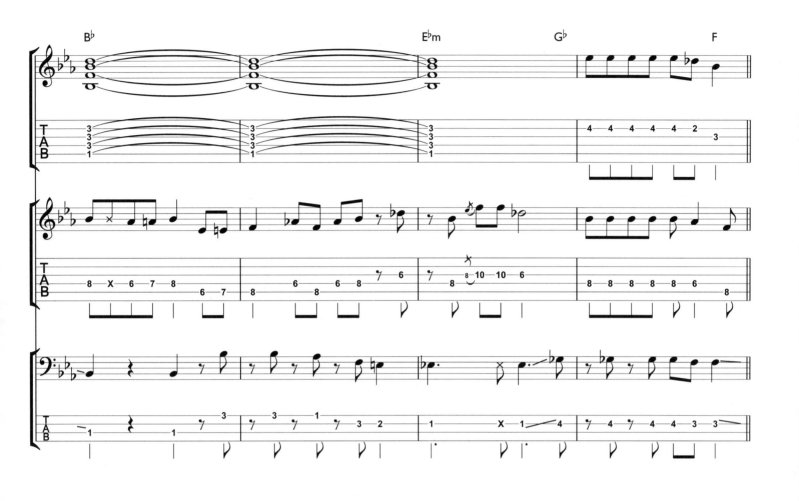

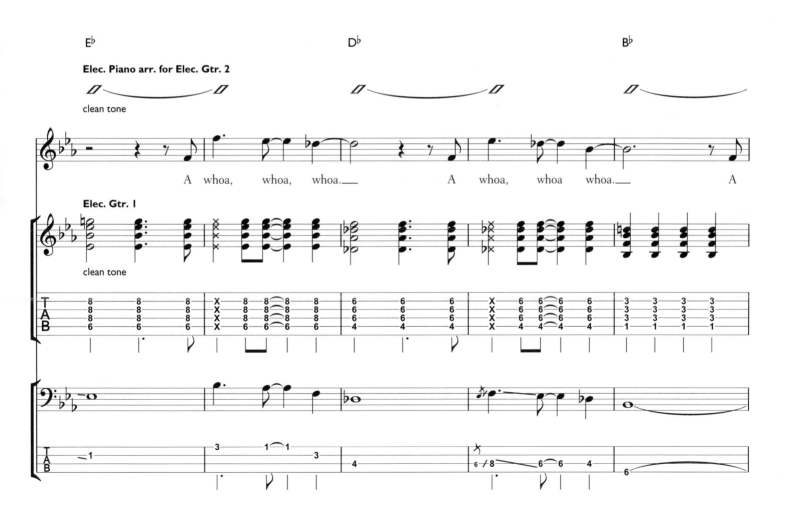

da da da da   da   da da da da   da da da da   da   da da.

A whoa, whoa, whoa.

Elec. Gtrs. 1 & 2

distortion

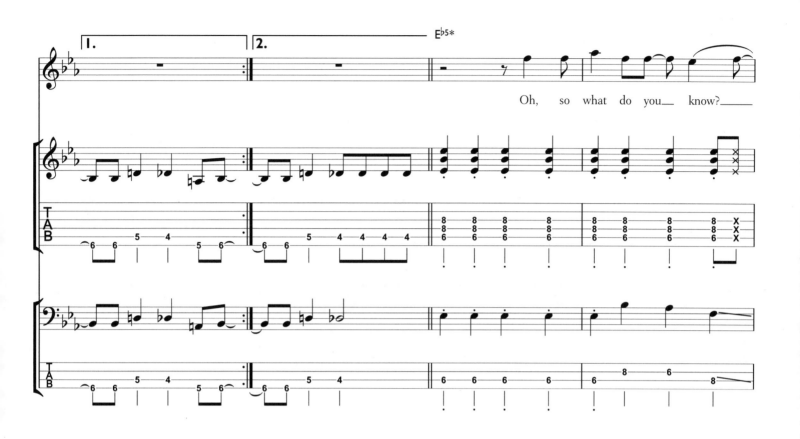

Oh, so what do you___ know?___

___ Yeah you don't know no-thing no.___ Yeah but I'll still take you home.___

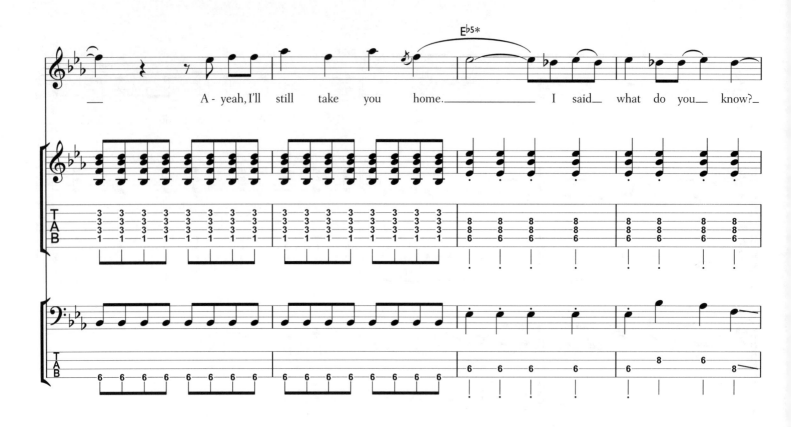

A - yeah, I'll still take you home._____ I said__ what do you__ know?_

Oh, you don't know no - thing. I_____ fan - cy you with a pas - sion, ah you're a

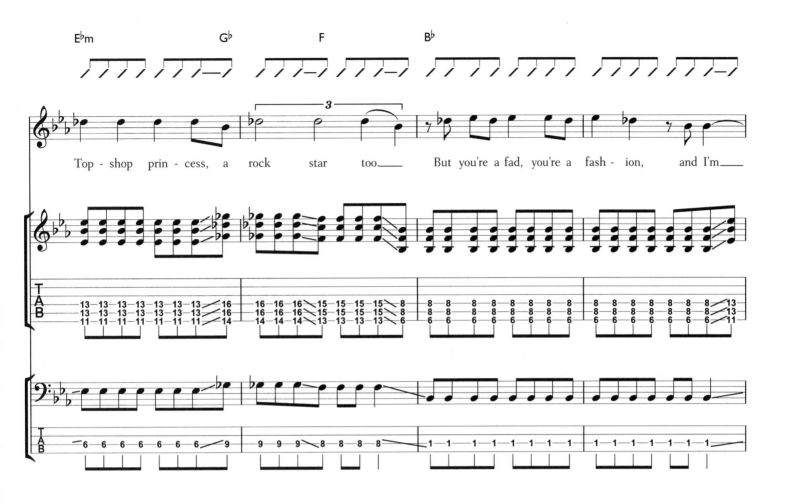

Top - shop prin - cess, a rock star too___ But you're a fad, you're a fash - ion, and I'm___

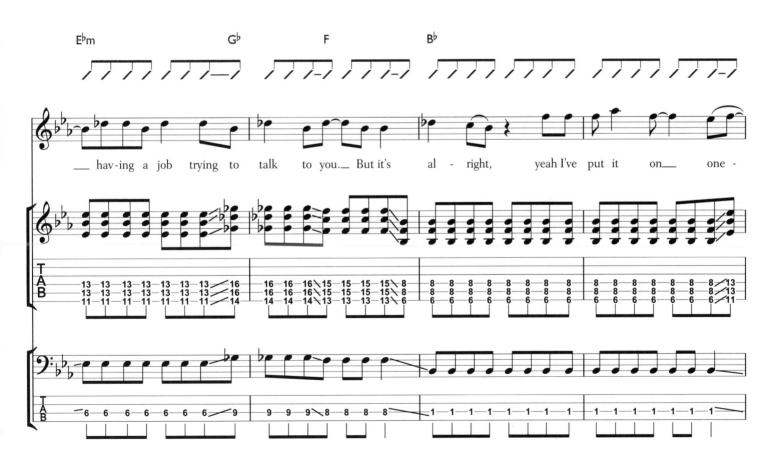

___ hav-ing a job trying to talk to you.___ But it's al - right, yeah I've put it on___ one -

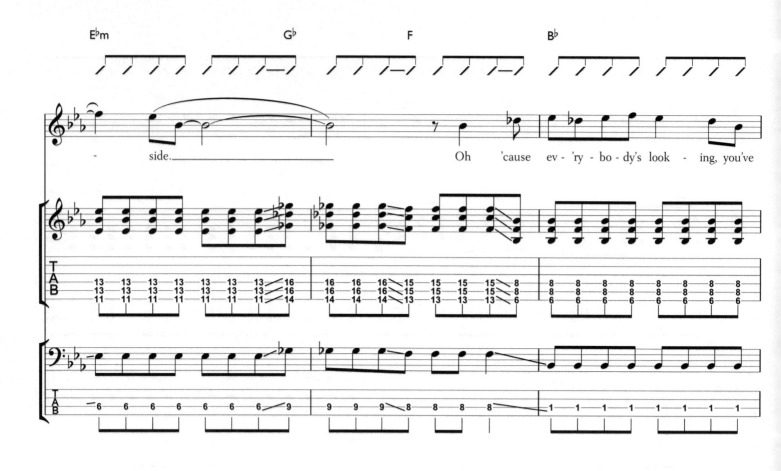

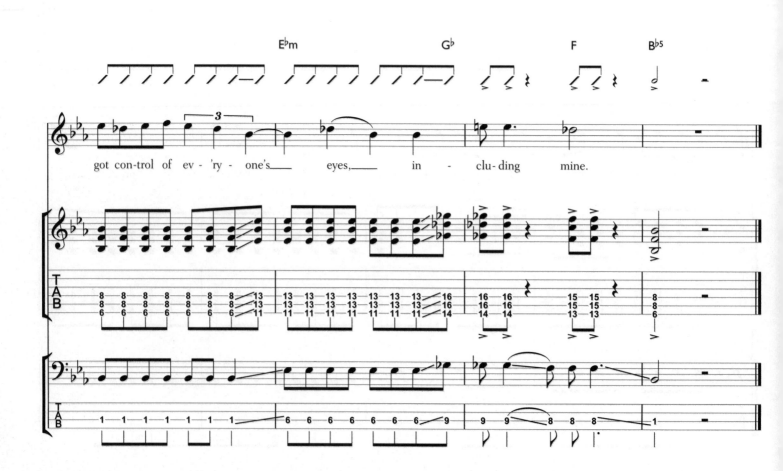

riot van

Words and Music by Alex Turner

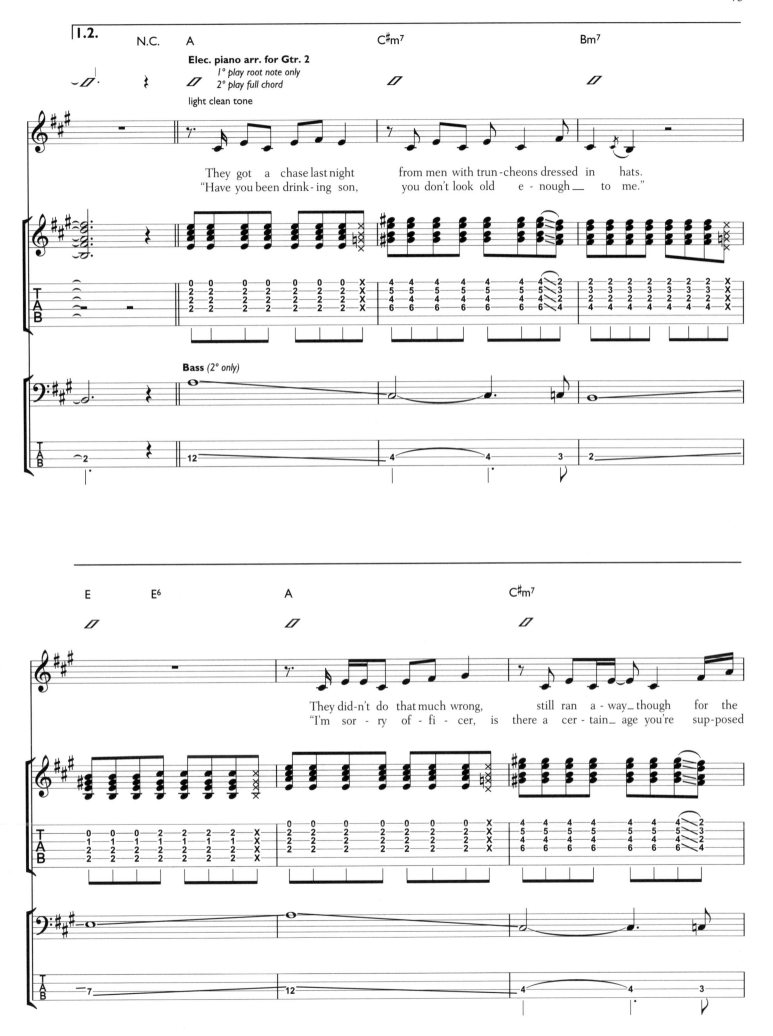

1.2.

N.C. A   C#m⁷   Bm⁷

Elec. piano arr. for Gtr. 2
1° play root note only
2° play full chord
light clean tone

They got a chase last night   from men with trun-cheons dressed in   hats.
"Have you been drink-ing son,   you don't look old   e - nough __ to me."

Bass *(2° only)*

E   E⁶   A   C#m⁷

They did-n't do that much wrong,   still ran a - way __ though   for the
"I'm sor - ry of - fi - cer,   is there a cer - tain __ age you're   sup-posed

red lights indicates doors are secured

Words and Music by Alex Turner

Well you're co-ming up at our end, aren't you? So I'll get one with you.

Oh won't he let us have six in?___ Es-pe-cially not with the food.

He could-a just told us no though, he dint have to be___ rude.

You see her in the__ green dress? She talked to me at the bar.__
Well how fun-ny was that sketch ear-li - er, up near that ta - xi rank.

Well, how come it's al - rea - dy two pound fif - ty? We've on - ly gone a - bout a yard.__
Oh no, you__ will have missed it, think it was when you went to the bank. These two

Oh dint ya see she were gor - geous, she was be-yond be - lief, but this
lads squar-ing up pro -per shout - ing 'bout who was next in the queue.

Elec. Gtr. 2 (2° only)

lad at the side drink - ing a Smir-noff ice came and paid for her tro-pi-cal Reef. And I'm
The kind of thing that would seem so sil - ly but not when they've both had a few. Well

And so why___ are they in a ta - xi? 'Cause I did-n't want to leave, I__ said it's

__High Green mate, vi - a Hills - bo - rough please.__

Drun - ken plots hatched to___ jump it,

Elec. Gtr. 2

overdrive

Elec. Gtr. 1

overdrive & heavy palm muting

N.C.

ask a- round, are ya sure?_ Went for it but the red light was show-ing, and the red_ light in-di-cates doors are se - cured.

mardy bum

Words and Music by Alex Turner

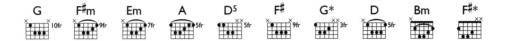

Well now then Mar-dy Bum,___ I see your frown and it's___like look-ing down the
Well now then Mar-dy Bum,___ oh I'm in___ trou-ble a-gain,___ aren't

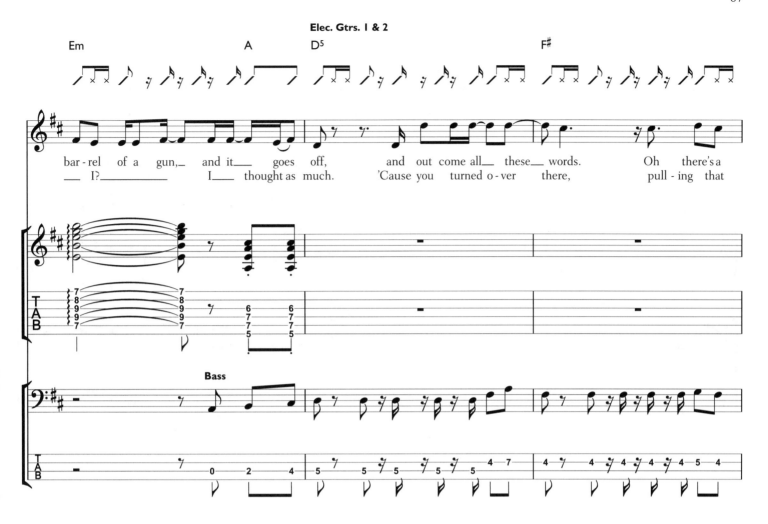

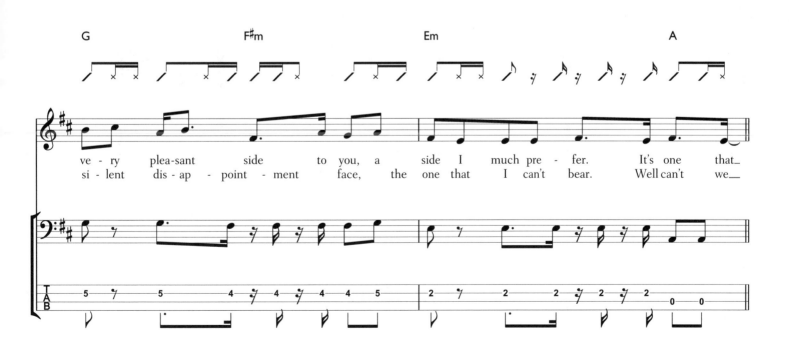

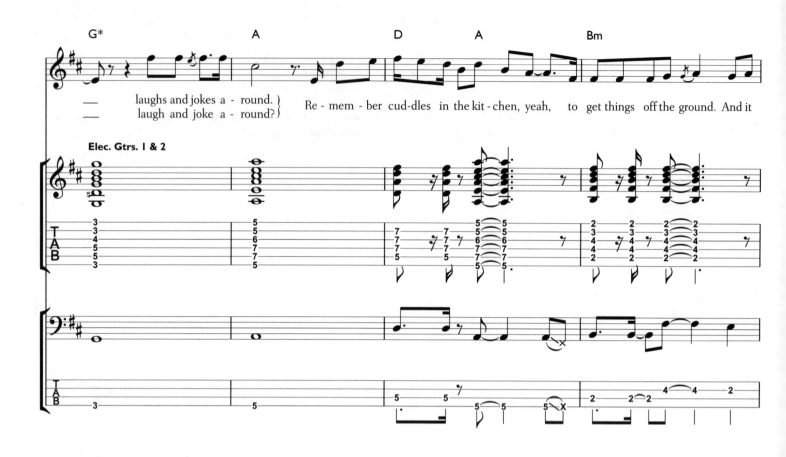

laughs and jokes a - round.)
laugh and joke a - round?)
Re - mem - ber cud-dles in the kit-chen, yeah, to get things off the ground. And it

was up, up and a - way. Oh, but it's right hard to re - mem - ber that_ on a day like to - day_ when you're

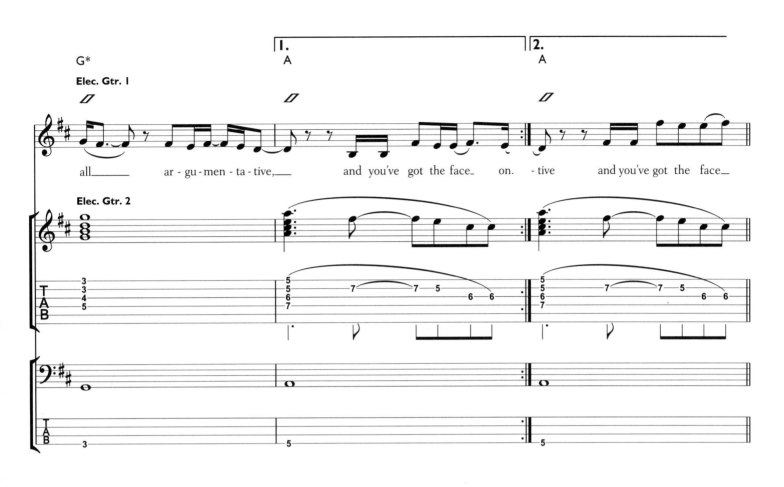

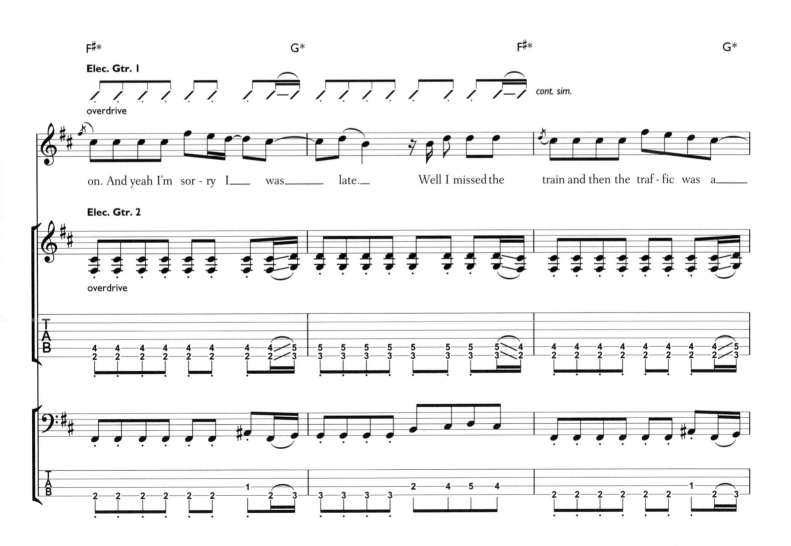

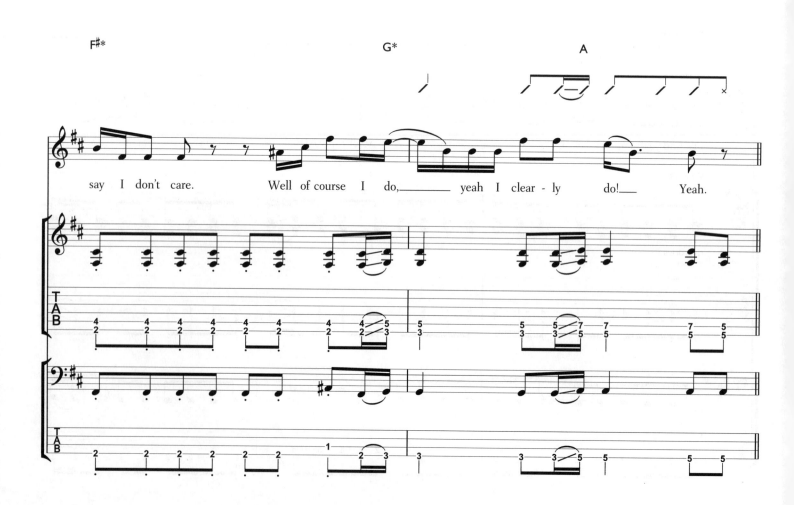

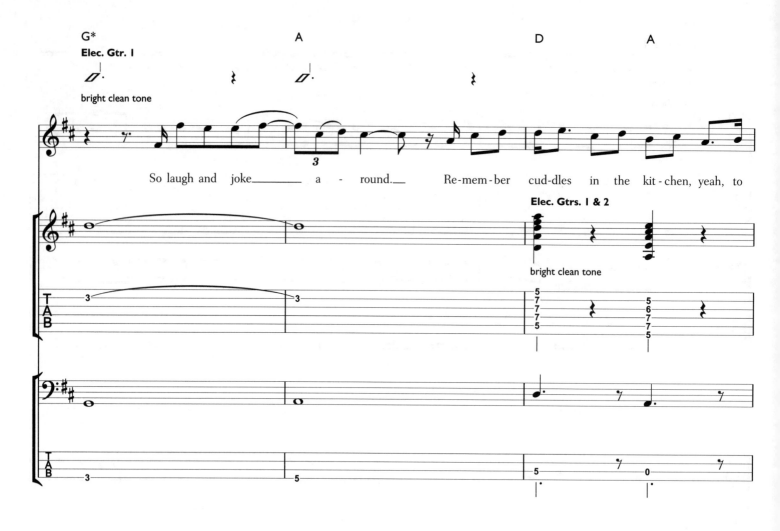

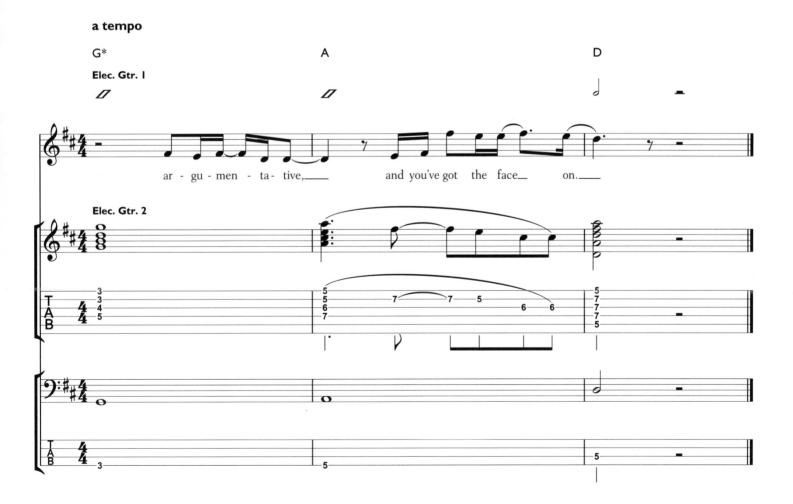

perhaps vampires is a bit strong but...

Words and Music by Alex Turner

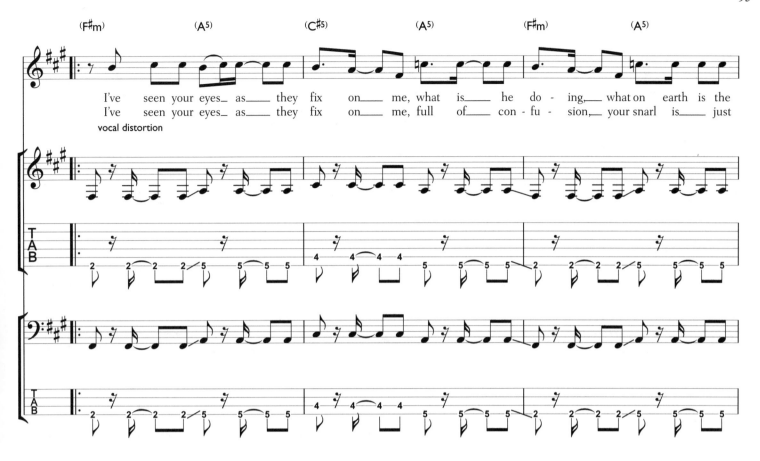

vocal distortion

I've seen your eyes__ as__ they fix on__ me, what is__ he do-ing,__ what on earth is the
I've seen your eyes__ as__ they fix on__ me, full of__ con - fu - sion,__ your snarl is__ just

plan, has__ he got one? You bet -ter give__ me__ some poin - ters__ since you are__ the
so con - de -scen - ding. Trying to ex - plain that__ we're on to__ a win__ if the

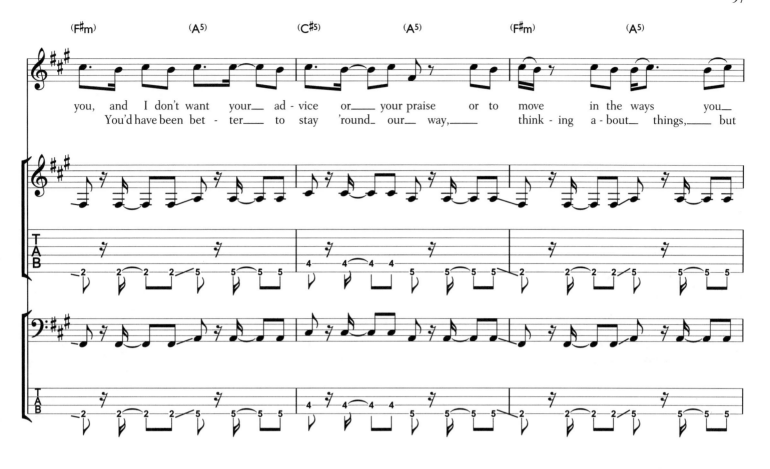

98

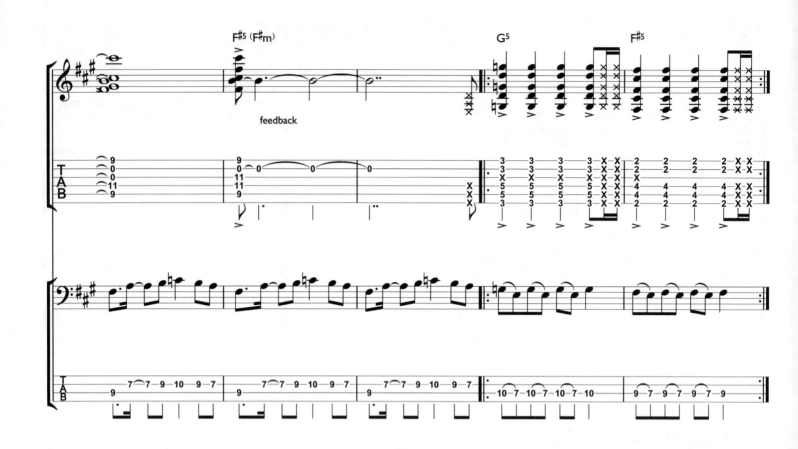

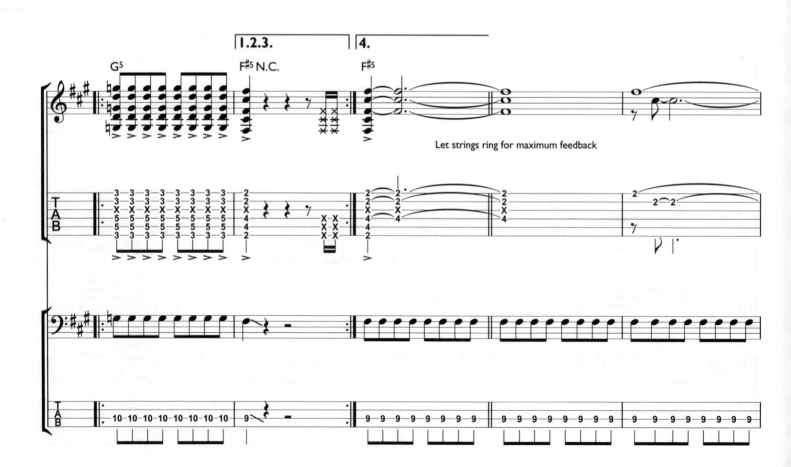

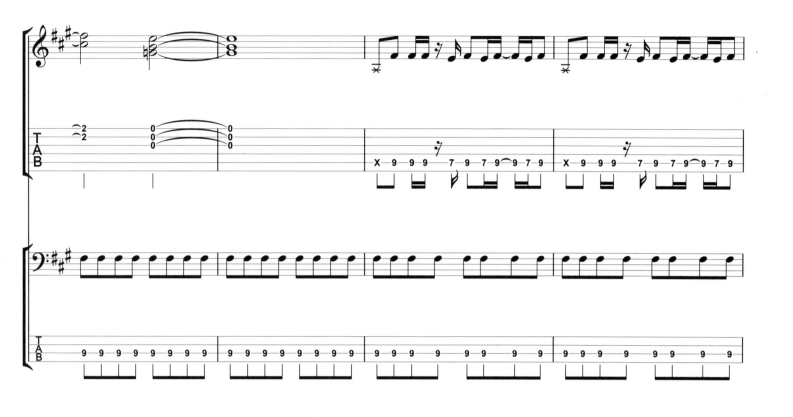

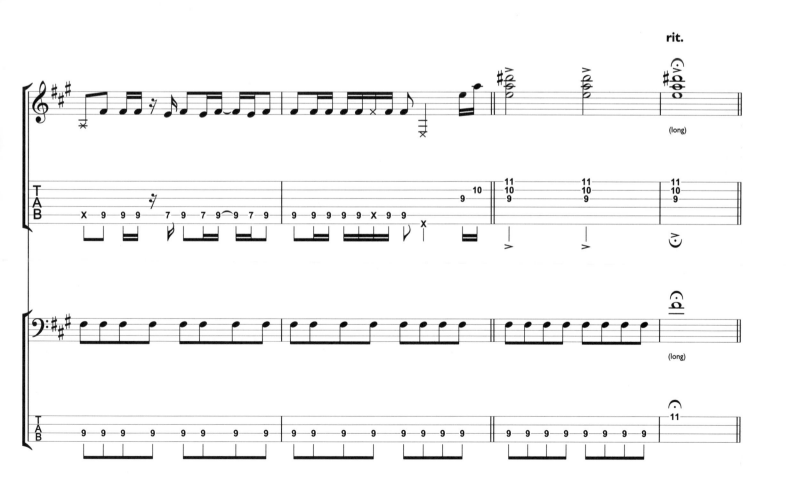

All you peo- ple__ are vam- pires!

when the sun goes down

Words and Music by Alex Turner

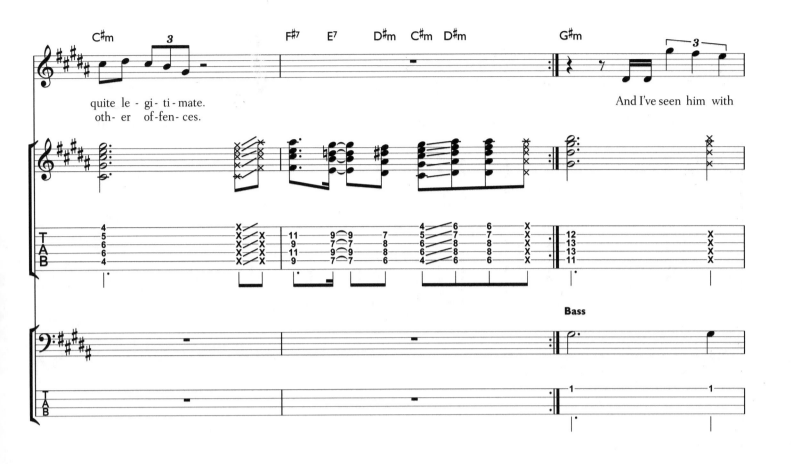

quite le - gi - ti - mate.
oth - er of - fen - ces.

And I've seen him with

girls of the night, and he told Rox - anne to put__ on her__ red light.

It's all in - fec - ted but he'll

be al- right,'cause he's a scum-bag don't you know. ___ I said he's a scum-bag don't you

know!

♩ = 170

Play section x3

Al - though you're try-ing not
Look, here comes a Ford

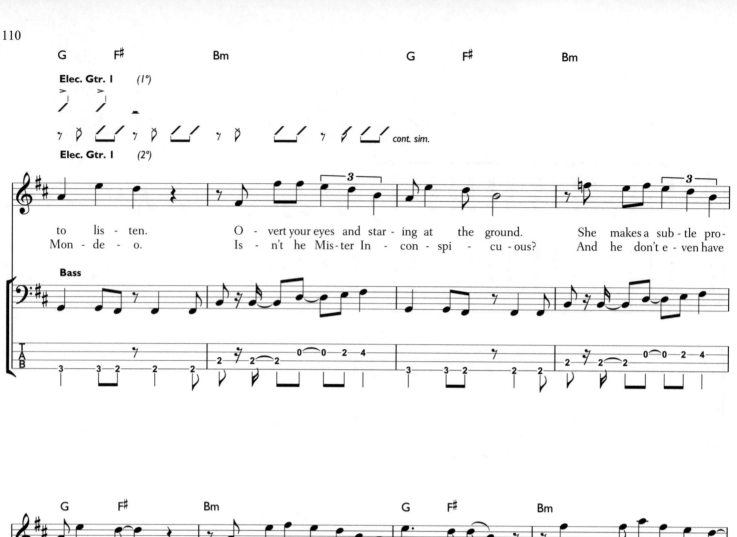

to lis - ten. O - vert your eyes and star - ing at the ground. She makes a sub - tle pro-
Mon - de - o. Is - n't he Mis-ter In - con - spi - cu - ous? And he don't e - ven have

-po - si - tion. "I'm sor-ry love, I'll have to turn you down." Oh he must be up to_
to say 'owt. She's in the stance rea-dy to get picked_ up. Bet she's de-ligh-ted when she

—— some - thing. What are the chan - ces, sure it's more than like - ly.
__ sees__ him. Pull - ing in and giv - ing her the eye.__

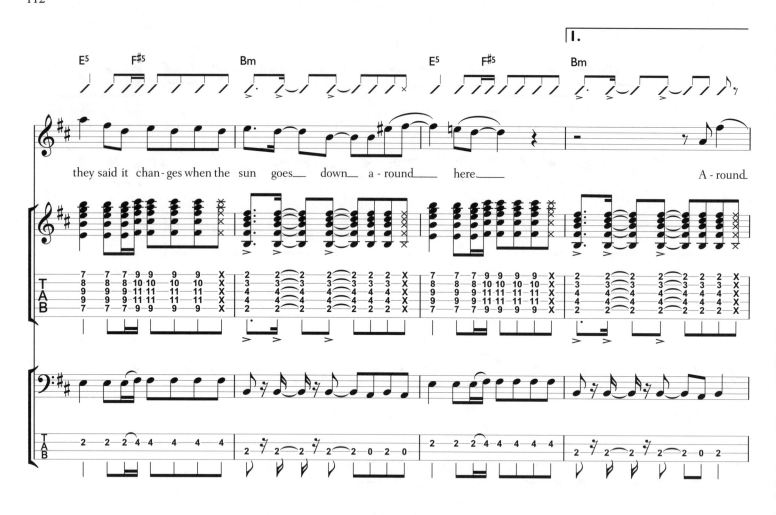

they said it chan-ges when the sun goes down a-round here A-round

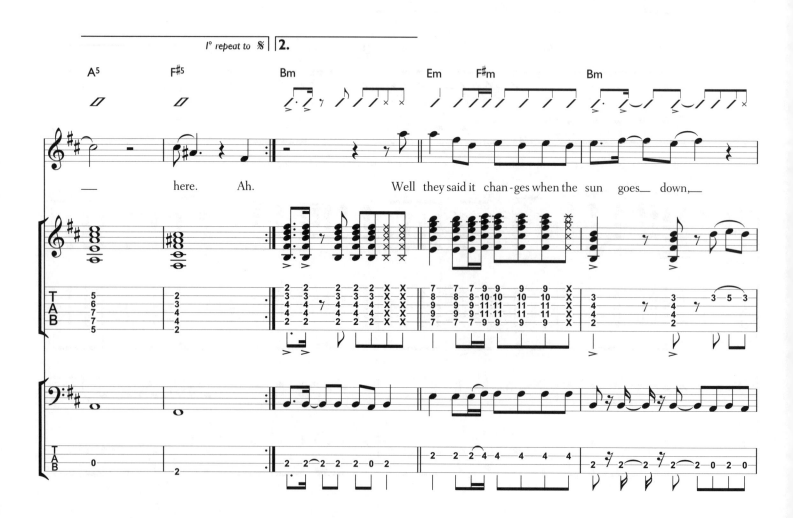

here. Ah. Well they said it chan-ges when the sun goes down,

from the ritz to the rubble

Words and Music by Alex Turner

re - a - lize then that it's fin - ally the time to walk back past ten thou-sand eyes in the line. And you can

swap jum - pers and make a - no-ther move, in - stilled in your brain you've got some-thing to prove to all

Elec. Gtr. 2

light overdrive

the smirk-ing fa-ces and the boys in black. Why — can't they be pleas- ant? Why can't they have a laugh? He's got his

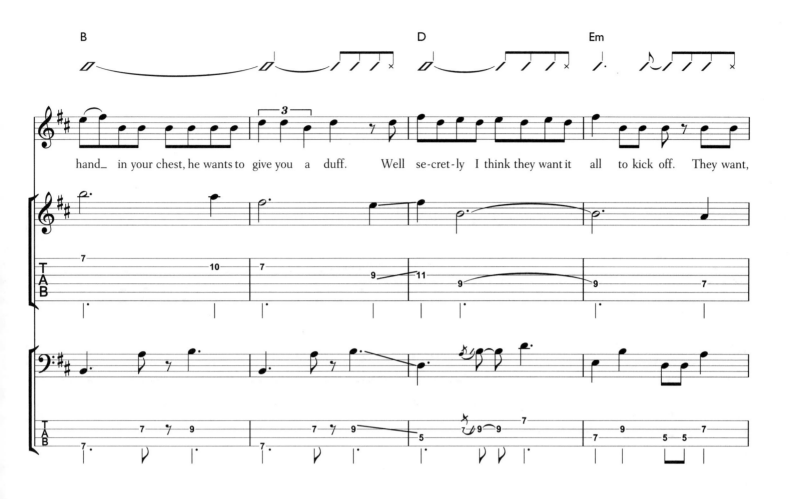

hand in your chest, he wants to give you a duff. Well se-cret-ly I think they want it all to kick off. They want,

arms fly-ing ev-'ry-where and bot-tles as well, it's just some-thing to talk a-bout, a sto-ry to tell you.

Well I'm so glad they turned us all a-way, we'll put it down

— to fate.— I thought a thou-sand mil-lion things that I could ne-ver think

120

was last night. You couldn't have done that on a___ Sun - day.
kissed last night. You couldn't have done that on a___ Sun - day. (Of course not.)

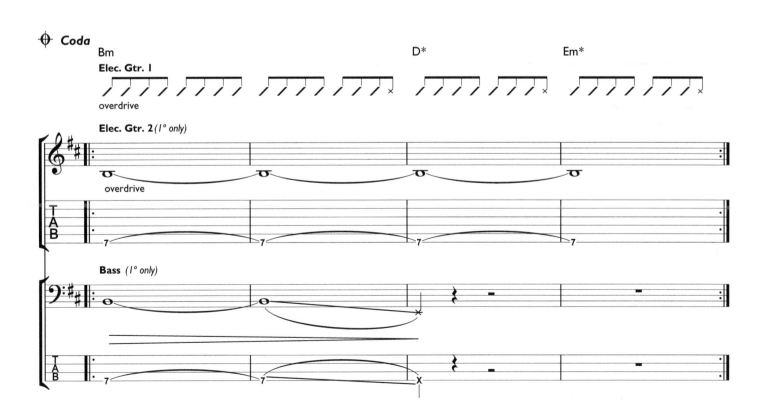

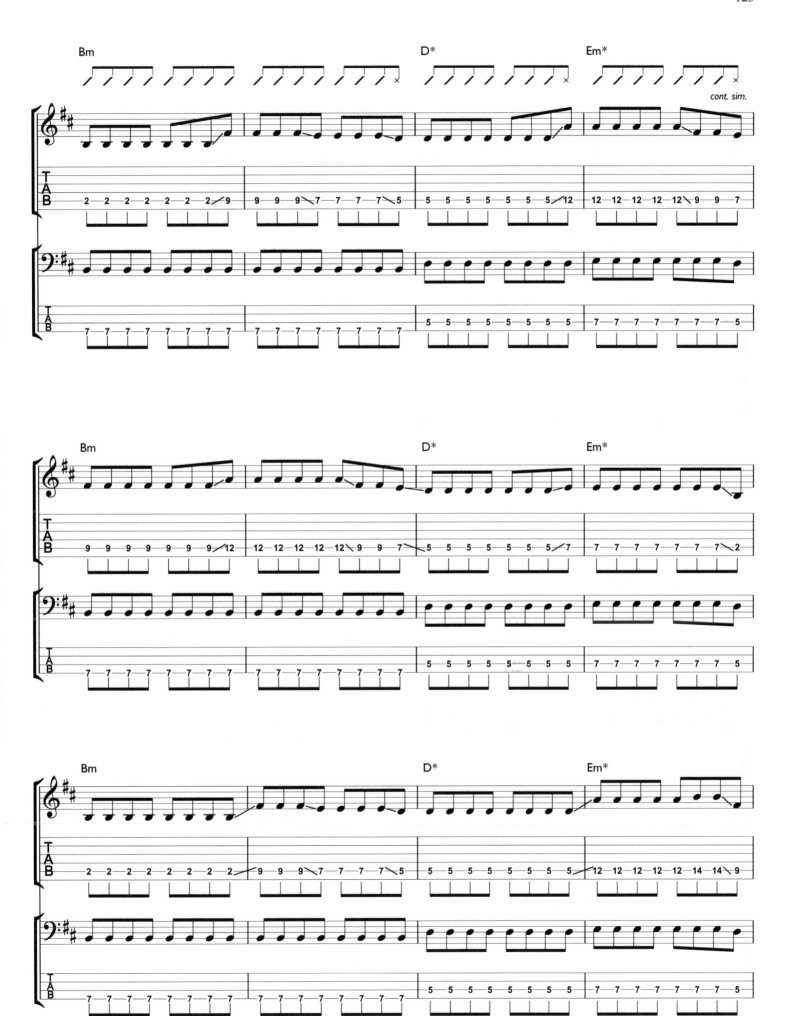

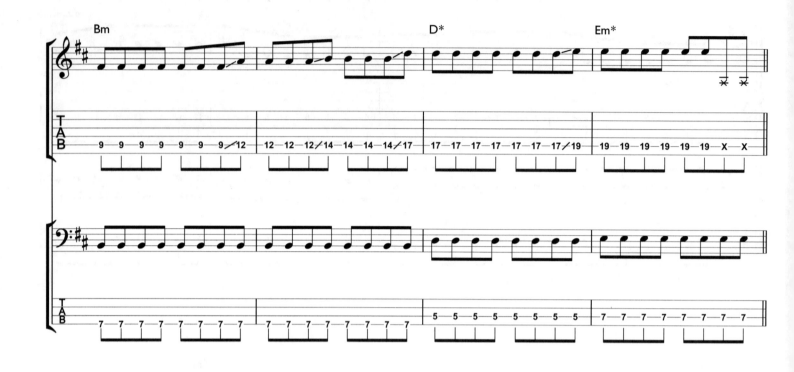

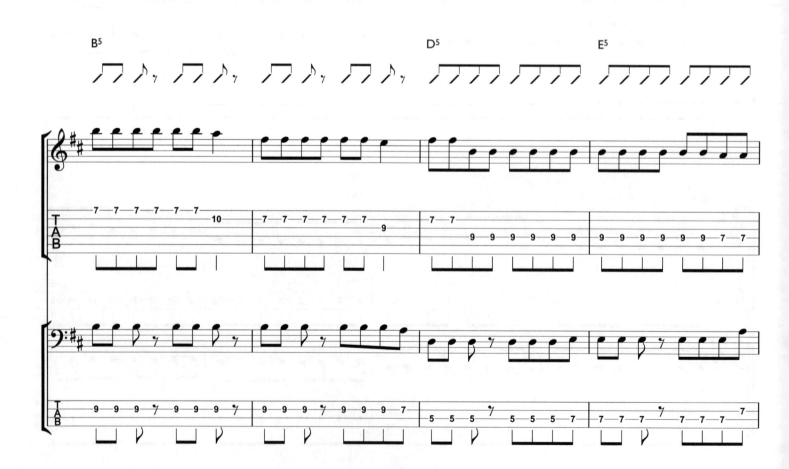

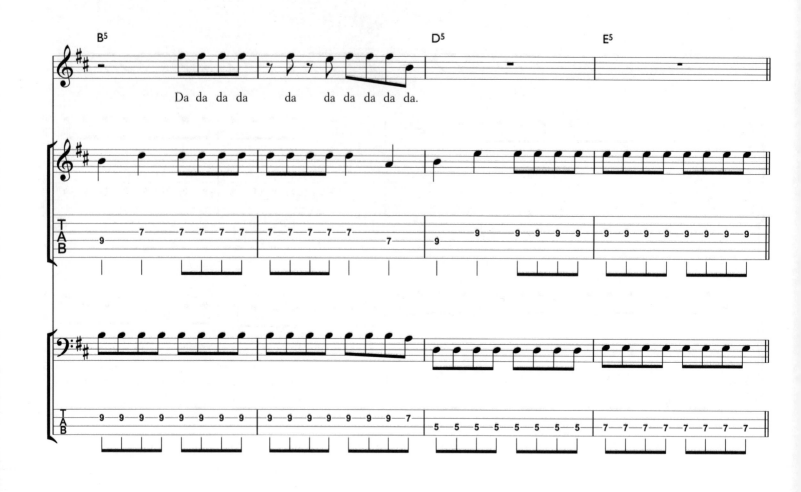

Da da da da   da   da da da da da.

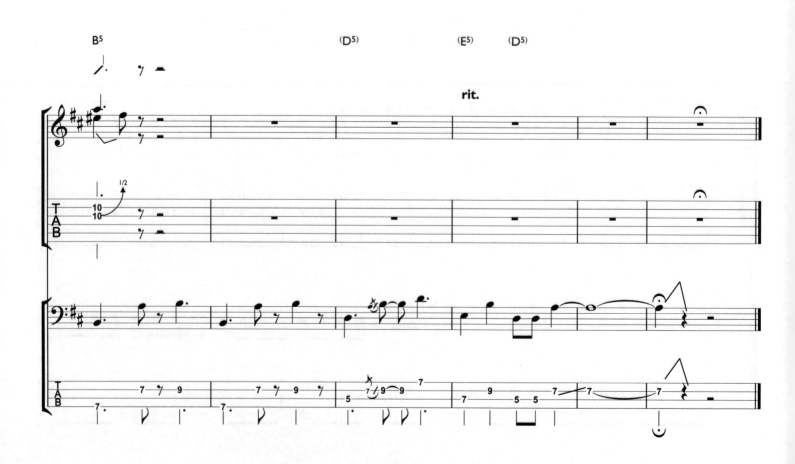

a certain romance

Words and Music by Alex Turner

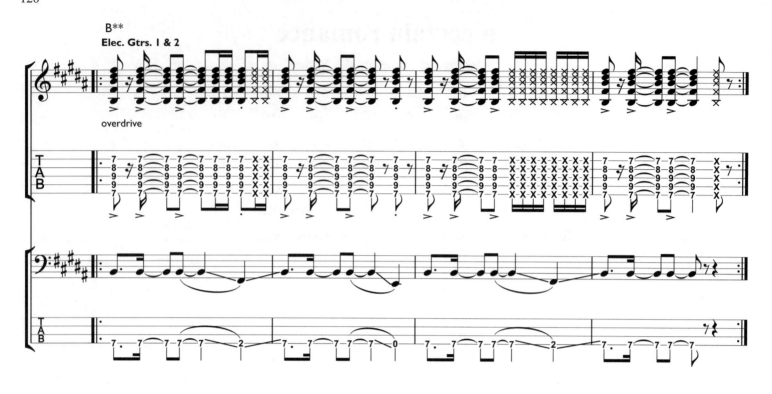

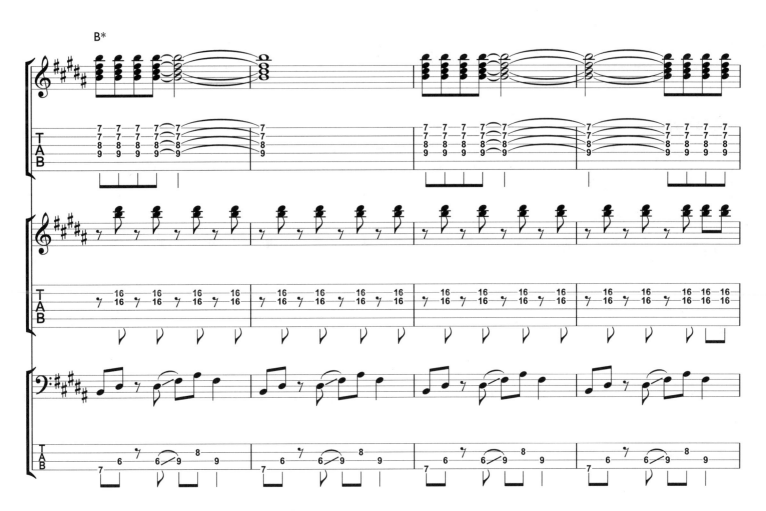

E

Em

B*

Elec. Gtr. 2 (1°) slightly dirty tone
Elec. Gtr. 2 (3°) plays and holds notes in parenthesis - slightly dirty tone

Elec. Gtr. 2 (2°) slightly dirty tone

Well oh they might wear clas - sic Ree - boks,__ or knack-ered__ Con - verse, or
O - ver there there's bro - ken bones. There's on - ly mu - sic, so
Well o - ver there there's friends of____ mine.__ What can I____ say,__ I've known them

Gtr. I (Elec.)

bright clean tone

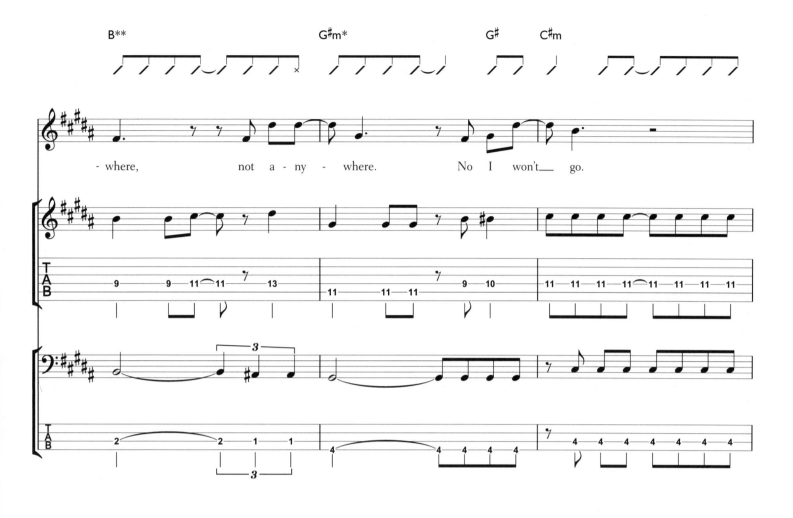

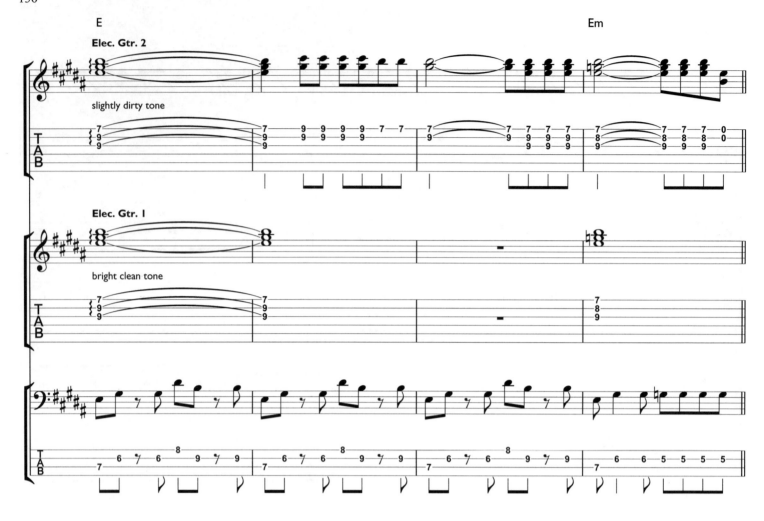

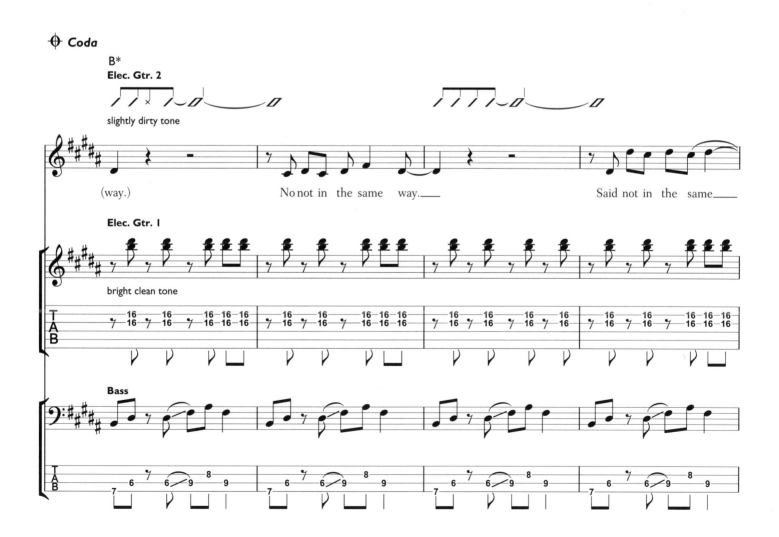

E   Em

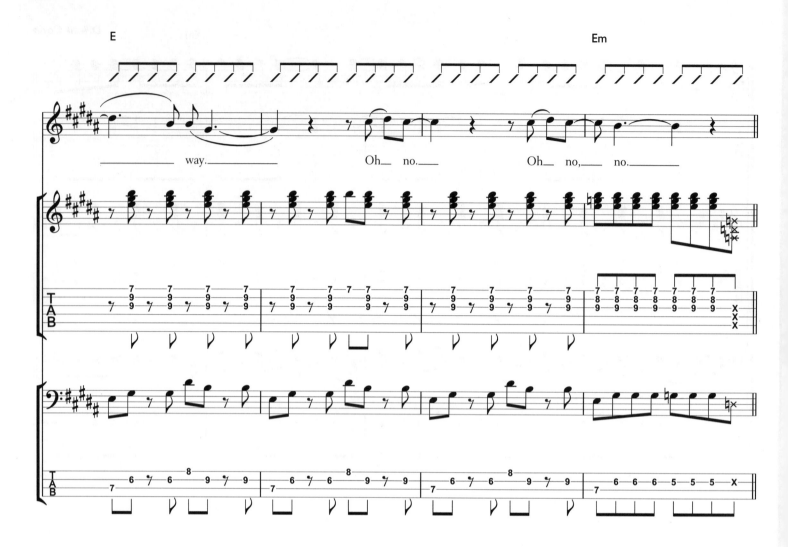

way.   Oh no.   Oh no, no.

B***

Elec. Gtr. 1

overdrive   cont. sim.

Elec. Gtr. 2   E**

overdrive

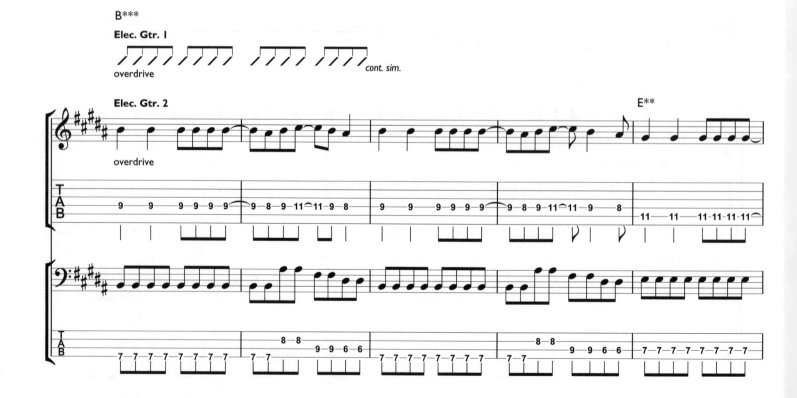

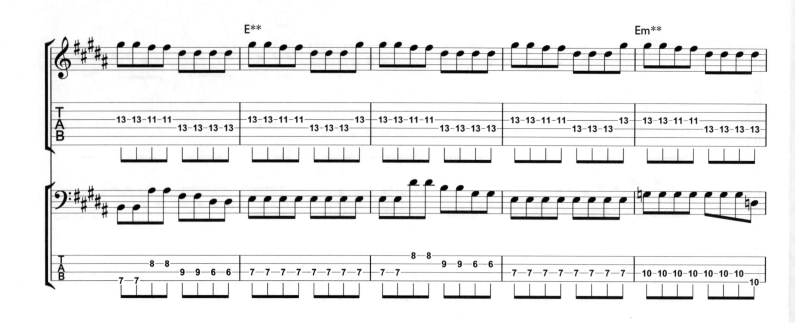

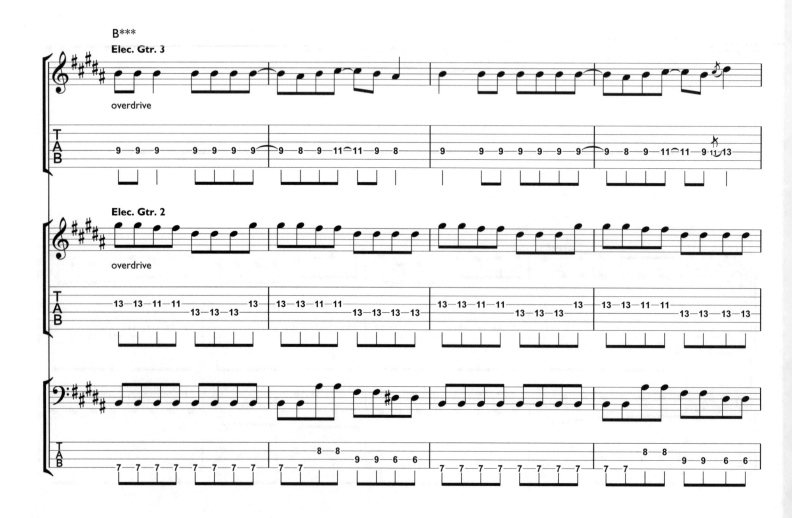

Notation and Tablature explained

Understanding chord boxes

Chord boxes show the neck of your guitar as if viewed head on—the vertical lines represent the strings (low E to high E, from left to right), and the horizontal lines represent the frets.

An **X** above a string means 'don't play this string'.
An **O** above a string means 'play this open string'.
The black dots show you where to put your fingers.

A curved line joining two dots on the fretboard represents a 'barre'. This means that you flatten one of your fingers (usually the first) so that you hold down all the strings between the two dots at the fret marked.

A fret marking at the side of the chord box shows you where chords that are played higher up the neck are located.

Tuning your guitar

The best way to tune your guitar is to use an electronic tuner. Alternatively, you can use relative tuning; this will ensure that your guitar is in tune with itself, but won't guarantee that you will be in tune with the original track (or any other musicians).

How to use relative tuning

Fret the low E string at the 5th fret and pluck; compare this with the sound of the open A string. The two notes should be in tune. If not, adjust the tuning of the A string until the two notes match.

Repeat this process for the other strings according to this diagram:

Note that the B string should match the note at the 4th fret of the G string, whereas all the other strings match the note at the 5th fret of the string below.

As a final check, ensure that the bottom E string and top E string are in tune with each other.

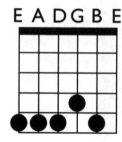

Detuning and Capo use

If the song uses an unconventional tuning, it will say so clearly at the top of the music, e.g. '6 = D' (tune string 6 to D) or 'detune guitar down by a semitone'. If a capo is used, it will tell you the fret number to which it must be attached. The standard notation will always be in the key at which the song sounds, but the guitar tab will take tuning changes into account. Just detune/add the capo and follow the fret numbers. The chord symbols will show the sounding chord above and the chord you actually play below in brackets.

Use of figures

In order to make the layout of scores clearer, figures that occur several times in a song will be numbered, e.g. 'Fig. 1', 'Fig. 2', etc.
A dotted line underneath shows the extent of the 'figure'. When a phrase is to be played, it will be marked clearly in the score, along with the instrument that should play it.

Reading Guitar Tab

Guitar tablature illustrates the six strings of the guitar graphically, showing you where you put your fingers for each note or chord. It is always shown with a stave in standard musical notation above it. The guitar tablature stave has six lines, each of them representing a different string. The top line is the high E string, the second line being the B string, and so on. Instead of using note heads, guitar tab uses numbers which show the fret number to be stopped by the left hand. The rhythm is indicated underneath the tab stave. Ex. 1 (below) shows four examples of single notes.

Ex. 2 shows four different chords. The 3rd one (Asus4) should be played as a barre chord at the 5th fret. The 4th chord (C9) is a half, or jazz chord shape. You have to mute the string marked with an 'x' (the A string in this case) with a finger of your fretting hand in order to obtain the correct voicing.

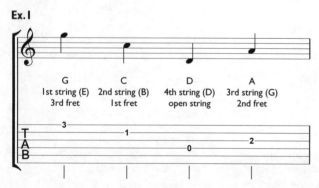

Notation of other guitar techniques

Picking hand techniques:

1. Down and up strokes
These symbols show that the first and third notes are to be played with a down stroke of the pick and the others up strokes.

2. Palm mute
Mute the notes with the palm of the picking hand by lightly touching the strings near the bridge.

3. Pick rake
Drag the pick across the indicated strings with a single sweep. The extra pressure will often mute the notes slightly and accentuate the final note.

4. Arpeggiated chords
Strum across the indicated strings in the direction of the arrow head of the wavy line.

5. Tremolo picking
Shown by the slashes on the stem of the note. Very fast alternate picking. Rapidly and continuously move the pick up and down on each note.

6. Pick scrape
Drag the edge of the pick up or down the lower strings to create a scraping sound.

7. Right hand tapping
'Tap' onto the note indicated by a '+' with a finger of the picking hand. It is nearly always followed by a pull-off to sound the note fretted below.

8. Tap slide
As with tapping, but the tapped note is slid randomly up the fretboard, then pulled off to the following note.

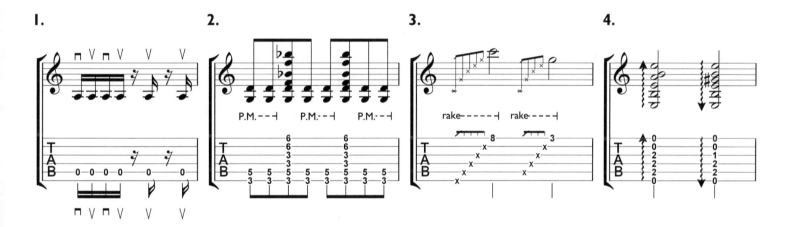

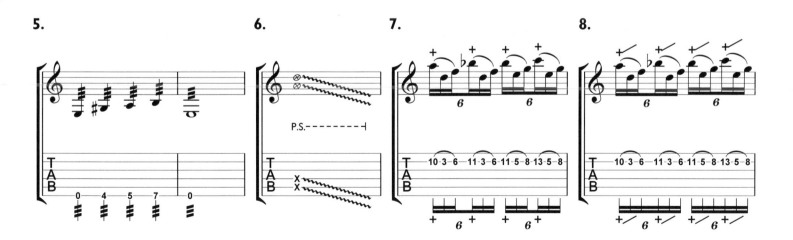

Fretting hand techniques:

1. Hammer-on and pull-off
These consist of two or more notes linked together by a slur. For hammer-ons, fret and play the lowest note, then 'hammer on' to the higher note with another finger. For a pull-off, play the highest note then 'pull off' to a lower note fretted with another finger. In both cases, only pick the first note.

2. Glissandi (slides)
Fret and pick the first note, then slide the finger up to the second note. If they are slurred together, do not re-pick the second note.

3. Slow glissando
Play the note(s) and slowly slide the finger(s) in the direction of the diagonal line(s).

4. Quick glissando
Play the note(s) and immediately slide the finger(s) in the direction of the diagonal line(s).

5. Trills
Play the note and rapidly alternate between this note and the nearest one above in the key signature. If a note in brackets is shown before, begin with this note.

6. Fret hand muting
Mute the notes with cross noteheads with the fretting hand.

7. Left hand tapping
Sound the note by tapping or hammering on to the note indicated by a 'o' with a finger of the fretting hand.

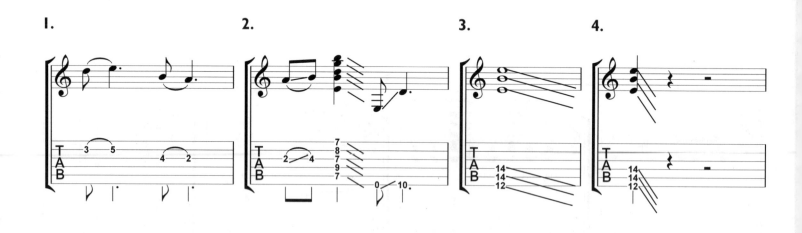

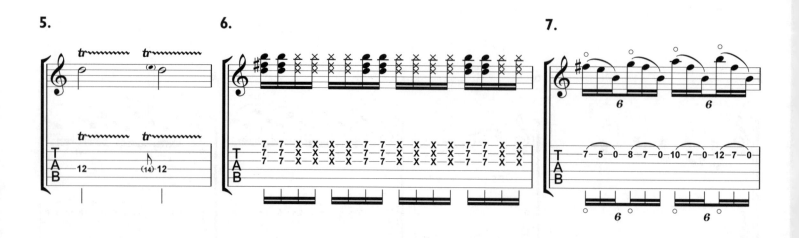

Bends and vibrato

Bends

Bends are shown by the curved arrow pointing to a number (in the tab).
Fret the first note and then bend the string up by the amount shown.

1. Semitone bend (half step bend)

The smallest conventional interval; equivalent to raising the note by one fret.

2. Whole tone bend (whole step bend)

Equivalent to two frets.

3. Minor third bend (whole step and a half)

Equivalent to three frets.

4. Microtonal bend (quarter-tone bend, Blues curl)

Bend by a slight degree, roughly equivalent to half a fret.

5. Bend and release

Fret and pick the first note. Bend up for the length of the note shown. May be followed by a release—letting the string fall back down to the original pitch.

6. Ghost bend (prebend)

Fret the bracketed note and bend quickly before picking the note.

7. Reverse bend

Fret the bracketed note and bend quickly before picking the note, immediately let fall back to the original.

8. Multiple bends

A series of bends and releases joined together. Only pick the first note.

9. Unison bend

Strike both indicated notes simultaneously and immediately bend the lower string up to the same pitch as the higher one.

10. Double note bend

Play both notes and bend simultaneously by the amount shown.

11. Bend involving more than one note

Bend first note and hold the bend whilst striking a note on another string.

12. Bends involving stationary notes

Play notes and bend lower string. Hold until release is indicated.

13. Vibrato

Shown by a wavy line. The fretting hand creates a vibrato effect using small, rapid up and down bends.

14. Bend and tap technique

Play and bend notes as shown, then sound final pitch by tapping onto note as indicated.

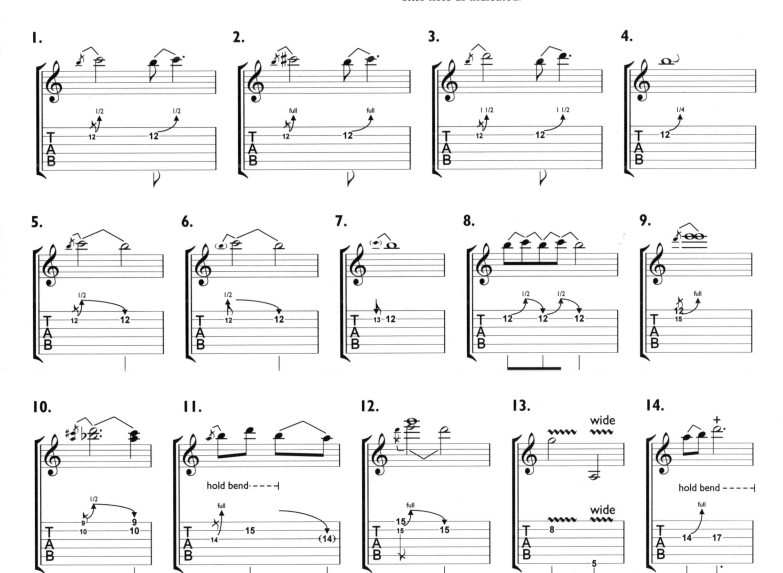

Tremolo arm (wammy bar)

1. Vibrato with tremolo arm
Create vibrato using small, rapid inflections of the tremolo arm.

2. Tremolo arm dive and return
Play note and depress tremolo arm by degree shown. Release arm to return to original note.

3. Tremolo arm scoop
Depress the arm just before picking the note and release.

4. Tremolo arm dip (or doop)
Pick the note, then lower the arm and quickly release.

5. Sustained note and dive bomb
Play note, hold for length of time shown and then depress arm to lower the pitch until the strings go slack.

6. Gargle
Pick the note and flick the tremolo arm rapidly with the same hand, making the pitch quiver.

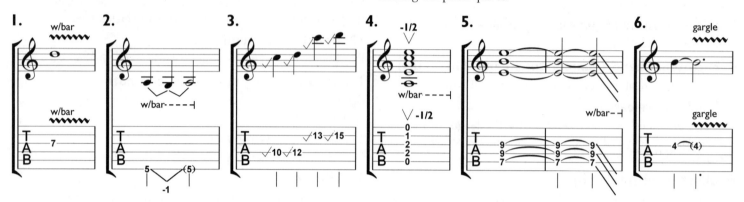

Harmonics & Other techniques

1. Natural harmonics
Instead of fretting properly, touch the string lightly with the fretting hand at the fret shown in the tab. Pick as normal. Diamond noteheads show the resultant pitch.

2. Artificial harmonics
The first tab number is fretted and held with the fretting hand as normal. The picking hand then produces a harmonic by using a finger to touch the string lightly at the fret shown by the bracketed number. Pick with another finger of the picking hand.

3. Pinched harmonics
Fret the note as shown, but create a harmonic by digging into the string with the side of the thumb as you pick it.

4. Tapped harmonics
Fret the note as shown, but create the harmonic through tapping lightly with the picking hand at the fret shown in brackets.

5. Touch harmonics
Fret the first note, hold it, then touch the string lightly at the fret shown at the end of the slur with the picking hand.

6. Violining
Turn the volume control to zero, pick the notes and then turn the control to fade the note in smoothly.

7. Fingering (fretting hand)
Small numbers show the finger with which each note is to be fretted.

8. Fingerpicking notation (PIMA)
Notation that shows which finger should be used to pick each note when playing finger style. p = thumb, i = index, m = middle, a = ring.

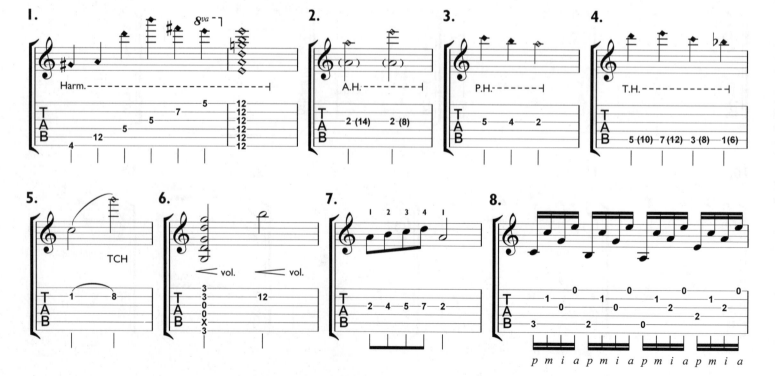